INSTRUCTOR'S RESOURCE MANUAL

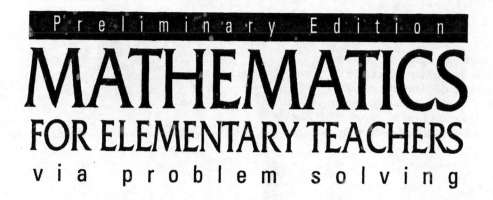

Preliminary Edition

MATHEMATICS
FOR ELEMENTARY TEACHERS
via problem solving

JOANNA O. MASINGILA
Syracuse University

FRANK K. LESTER
Indiana University

PRENTICE HALL Upper Saddle River, NJ 07458

Supplements Editor: *April Thrower*
Production Editor: *Shea Oakley*
Manufacturing Buyer: *Alan Fischer*
Special Projects Manager: *Barbara A. Murray*
Supplements Cover Manager: *Paul Gourhan*
Cover Designer: *Liz Nemeth*

© 1998 by **PRENTICE-HALL, INC.**
Simon & Schuster/A Viacom Company
Upper Saddle River, NJ 07458

Printed in the United States of America

10 9 8 7 6 5 4 3 2

ISBN 0-13-889189-3

Prentice-Hall International (UK) Limited, *London*
Prentice-Hall of Australia Pty. Limited, *Sydney*
Prentice-Hall Canada, Inc., *Toronto*
Prentice-Hall Hispanoamericana, S.A., *Mexico*
Prentice-Hall of India Private Limited, *New Delhi*
Prentice-Hall of Japan, Inc., *Tokyo*
Simon & Schuster Asia Pte. Ltd., *Singapore*
Editora Prentice-Hall do Brasil, Ltda., *Rio de Janeiro*

BRIEF CONTENTS

CONTENTS

Chapter 7:   Real Numbers: Rationals & Irrationals   **127**

Chapter 8:   Patterns & Functions   **145**

Analytic and Transformational Geometry

Tessellations

Answers to Exercises and More Problems   **227**

PREFACE

The nature of mathematics instruction has changed rather dramatically in recent years due in large part to the spirit of reform that is prominent in recent school mathematics curriculum development efforts. In the past, mathematics instruction was viewed by many as an activity in which an "expert" attempted to transmit her or his knowledge of mathematics to a group of mostly passive students. This passive transmission view has been replaced by one involving students as active participants in the act of "doing"—that is, creating, exploring, testing, verifying, etc.— mathematics. The new view that has emerged is one where mathematics is seen as a cooperative venture among students in which they are encouraged to explore, make and debate conjectures, build connections among concepts, solve problems growing out of their explorations, and construct personal meaning from all of these experiences. By adopting this new view, one also adopts a new way of thinking about the sort of collegiate mathematics instruction prospective elementary teachers should experience.

We began collaborating on the development of the materials in this book in 1988. At that time, with funding from the National Science Foundation, we were part of a team of mathematicians and mathematics educators whose task it was to create new courses. Subsequently, additional materials were developed by Joanna Masingila and several of her colleagues at Syracuse University beginning in 1995, as part of another project funded by the National Science Foundation. Both of us have continued to revise existing activities and develop new ones.

Principals Guiding the Development of the Materials

The activities contained in our books have been created with the new view of mathematics teaching and learning promoted by the American Mathematical Association of Two-Year Colleges (AMATYC) and the National Council of Teachers of Mathematics (NCTM). In particular, we developed the materials with the following documents in mind: AMATYC's publication, *Crossroads in Mathematics: Standards for Introductory College Mathematics Before Calculus*, and the NCTM's publications, *Curriculum and Evaluation Standards for School Mathematics*, *Professional Standards for Teaching Mathematics, and Assessment Standards for School Mathematics*. These documents led us to identify six principals to guide our development efforts:

- *All Activities Are Based on the NCTM Standards.*

  Special emphasis is placed on the four primary standards of the NCTM: *problem solving, communication, reasoning*, and *connections*. First and foremost, students should be engaged in the solution of thought provoking, real world problems. Not only should students learn to solve problems, but they should also learn mathematics *via* problem solving. The second major standard is *communication*. Knowing mathematics is of little value if one cannot communicate mathematical ideas to other people. NCTM's third major standard is *reasoning*. Among other things, reasoning deals with the ability to think through a problem and to carefully evaluate any solution that has been proposed. The fourth of the major standards involves making *connections*. To really understand mathematics, one must be able to see connections between various mathematical ideas, and between "school" and "real world" mathematics.

- *Solving Problems Regularly and Often Is an Essential Part of Developing a Good Understanding of Mathematics.*

  In order for you to improve your ability to solve mathematics problems, you must attempt to solve a variety of types of problems on a regular basis and over a prolonged period of time. We also believe that ability to solve problems goes hand-in-hand with the development of an understanding of mathematical concepts, procedures, and skills. Put another way, as you solve problems you will develop better understanding of the mathematics involved in the problems. And, as you develop better understanding of mathematical ideas, you will become a better problem solver.

- *Problem Solving Involves a Very Complex Set of Processes.*

  There is a dynamic interaction between mathematical concepts and the processes used to solve problems involving those concepts. That is, heuristics, procedural skills, control processes, awareness of one's cognitive processes, etc. develop concurrently with the development of an understanding of mathematical concepts.

- *The Teacher's Role in Fostering Healthy Problem-solving Performance Is Vitally Important.*

  Problem-solving instruction is likely to be most effective when it is provided in a systematically organized manner under the direction of the teacher. Our philosophy is that the role of the teacher changes from that of a "dispenser of knowledge" to a "facilitator of learning." With respect to problem solving and reasoning, this implies that the teacher does very little lecturing on how to solve specific types of problems and much more posing and discussing of a wide variety of non-routine and applied problems. The teacher also focuses on helping you make connections between the mathematics you are learning and its application to the workplace or home.

- *Cooperative, Small-group Work Is Encouraged.*

  The standard arrangement for working on the activities in the *Activity Book* is for you to work in small groups. Small group work is especially appropriate for activities involving new content (e.g., new mathematics topics, new problem-solving strategies) or when the focus of the activity is on the process of solving problems (e.g., planning, decision making, assessing progress) or exploring mathematical ideas.

- *Assessment Practices Are Closely Connected to Instructional Emphases.*

  We believe that the teacher's instructional plan should include attention to how your performance will be assessed. In order for you to become convinced of the importance of the sort of behaviors that a good problem-solving program promotes, it is necessary to use assessment techniques that reward such behaviors. As a result, we encourage teachers to use various alternative assessment methods such as providing opportunities during tests for you to work with a group of your classmates to solve certain problems on the tests. We also encourage teachers to assess your ability to discuss your understanding of mathematical concepts and procedures in writing and orally.

How Are Our Materials Different from Other Mathematics Books?

You will quickly notice that the activities in the *Activity Book* are quite different from traditional sets of materials: *big mathematical ideas* serve as course organizers, *cooperative small group work* on the activities is expected, *reflective writing* is required of all students, *alternative assessment* procedures are used, and *teachers and students assume different roles.*

Big Mathematical Ideas

The term " big idea" refers to those themes that pervade several areas of mathematics and which serve to make connections among mathematics topics. These big ideas, then, are recurring, unifying themes in mathematics. With respect to identifying KEY big ideas to emphasize in a course or courses, we determined that it does not matter a great deal which ones are chosen. Instead, what matters is that a big idea should:

1. Help students make connections among what may for them seem like unrelated mathematical topics;
2. Help students make connections between the world of mathematics and the "real world," and
3. Provide ample opportunities for students to come to have a greater appreciation for and understanding of the beauty and subtlety of mathematics and mathematical activity.

Cooperative Learning

The philosophy of the materials requires that students—rather than the teacher— must bear the primary burden for constructing mathematical arguments and for providing mathematical explanations. Shifting the burden of explanation in this way is accomplished by organizing each class in a very different way from the usual university mathematics class: During much of each class period students work cooperatively in small groups to wrestle with problems that challenge them, to develop new and deeper understandings of fundamental mathematical concepts, and to talk about their new ways of thinking.

Reflective Thinking and Writing

Inside the classroom, students reflect as they work to understand a problem, evaluate their solution processes, decide if their solutions make sense, justify their generalizations, connect mathematical concepts, understand a problem solution different from their own, extend a problem, monitor their thinking processes, and communicate their ideas to other students and the teacher. When students are encouraged and expected to be reflective in their work, they become better at thinking reflectively, their understanding of the content improves, they are more creative and insightful in their problem solving, their motivation for learning increases, and they begin to look for, and make, connections between mathematical concepts. Outside of the classroom students can continue their reflective activity through reflective writing. Reflective thinking and writing are meaning-making processes that involve the learner in actively building connections between what he or she is learning and what is already known.

Alternative Assessment Practices

In addition to assessing students in order to assign grades, another just as important reason for assessment is to help the instructor build an accurate mental picture of the understandings held by students and to enable him or her to adjust instruction accordingly. Thus, assessment is an ongoing process in the classroom. Another source of assessment data for the instructor is the students' reflective writing. By reading students' writing an instructor gets additional insight into which topics have been understood and which need more attention or a more focused discussion. Still another reason for assessment is to indicate to students what is considered important. Because being able to communicate about mathematics is an important goal of the course, instructors must allow sufficient time for students to talk about mathematics and to write about it. And they must offer thoughtful reactions to students' communicative efforts, so that the students can see that their efforts to explain their ideas are valued.

Different Roles for Both Teacher and Students

The traditional mathematics classroom is teacher-centered. This type of instruction implies that there is a specific mathematical knowledge that the teacher has and through modeling what the teacher does and through passive absorption, students will acquire this knowledge. Research findings, however, indicate that learning occurs as students actively assimilate new information and construct their own meanings (Grouws, 1992; *Journal for Research in Mathematics Education*, 1994). Students engage in a great deal of invention in learning mathematics and impose their own interpretation on their experiences. Knowledge is an understanding that is created through active learning. Consequently, each student's knowledge of mathematics is uniquely personal. This means that mathematics classrooms should be more student-centered. As we envision the classroom, the students' role must be an involved, active one. Students are expected to listen to, respond to, and question the teacher and one another. They should also be reflective thinkers to become aware of how they themselves learn mathematics. Validity of particular representations and solutions should be determined by mathematical evidence and argument, whether working in large or small groups, and not be seeking the "right" answer from the teacher.

The overarching responsibility of the teacher is to establish a mathematical community in the classroom where everyone's thinking is respected and in which reasoning and discussing mathematical ideas and meanings is the norm. Within this community, the teacher's insightful questioning can play an important role in stimulating student thinking so that there are opportunities for students to examine and question their beliefs about mathematics, to have their misconceptions challenged, and to seek clarifications, strategies, and verifications without direct teacher intervention.

Special Features of the Materials

Our materials are comprised of three books—*Activity Book, Resource Manual*, and an *Instructor Manual*—and each has some special features as described below.

Activity Book

The *Activity Book* contains a matrix that depicts how the topics included in the *Activity Book* correlate with those found in several of the most popular traditional mathematics textbooks for prospective elementary teachers.

In addition to containing very different sorts of activities (as described above), each chapter also contains some special features that distinguish the book from more traditional books. In particular, each chapter includes a chapter overview and outline, a list of "Words, Concepts, and Procedures to Know," and sets of exercises and problems to supplement those found in the activities. Solutions to the odd numbered exercises and problems are found at the end of the book.

Resource Manual

Special features for the *Resource Manual* include: a chapter overview and outline, various historical, social, and cultural notes, explanations of mathematical concepts and procedures found in the *Activity Book*, a section titled "Where Would I Find This?", and a bibliography of key articles and books related to topics considered in the chapter. The "Where Would I Find This?" section of a chapter contains sample pages from elementary school textbooks that involve the topics of the chapter. *[This feature will not appear until the first edition of the book.]* Finally, a glossary and an index are included at the end of the *Resource Manual*.

Instructor Manual

The *Instructor Manual* contains a matrix that depicts how the topics included in the *Activity Book* correlate with those found in several of the most popular traditional mathematics textbooks for prospective elementary teachers. In addition, the *Instructor Manual* contains discussion notes and solutions for each activity, and solutions to all exercises and problems included in the *Activity Book*.

References

American Mathematical Association of Two-Year Colleges. (1995). *Crossroads in Mathematics: Standards for Introductory College Mathematics Before Calculus.* Memphis, TN: Author.

Grouws, D. A. (Ed.). (1994). *Handbook of Research on Mathematics Teaching and Learning.* New York: Macmillan.

Journal for Research in Mathematics Education. (1994, December). Special 25th Anniversary Issue.

National Council of Teachers of Mathematics. (1989). *Curriculum and Evaluation Standards for School Mathematics.* Reston, VA: Author.

National Council of Teachers of Mathematics. (1991). *Professional Standards for Teaching Mathematics.* Reston, VA: Author.

National Council of Teachers of Mathematics. (1995). *Assessment Standards for School Mathematics.* Reston, VA: Author.

Joanna O. Masingila

Frank K. Lester

Comparison of Topics in Traditional Books with Topics in our
Activity Book and *Resource Manual*

Traditional Chapters	Traditional Topics	Where Found in *Activity Book*	Where Found in *Resource Manual*
Introduction to Problem Solving	The Problem Solving Process	Chapter 0; Activities 1.1-1.10	Chapter 1 Explanations
	Strategies	Activities 1.1-1.10	Chapter 0; Chapter 1 Explanations
			Additional Items: Historical/Social/ Cultural Notes on Problem Solving
Sets, Functions, and Logic	Describing Sets		
	Set Operations		
	Functions	Activities 8.7	Chapter 8 Explanations
	Logic		
		Additional Items: Activities 8.1-8.6, 8.8-8.14 that explore patterns and functions	*Additional Items:* Historical/Social/ Cultural Notes on Patterns and Functions
Numeration Systems	Numeration Systems	Activities 2.1-2.5	Historical/Social/ Cultural Notes on Numeration
	Addition and Subtraction of Whole Numbers	Activity 3.3	Chapter 2 and 3 Explanations
	Multiplication and Division of Whole Numbers	Activity 3.3	Chapter 2 and 3 Explanations
	Algorithms for Whole-number Addition and Subtraction	Activities 3.6, 3.8, 3.9	Chapter 3 Explanations
	Algorithms for Whole-number Multiplication and Division	Activities 3.7, 3.10	Chapter 3 Explanations
		Additional Items: Activities 2.6-2.10 that explore place value ideas through different bases; Activities 3.1-3.2 that explore sets of numbers and their properties; Activities 3.11-3.12 that use algorithms to solve problems	*Additional Items:* Explanations on Numeration Ideas; Historical/Social/ Cultural Notes on Operations

Integers and Number Theory	Integers and Operations of Addition and Subtraction	Activities 3.4	Chapter 3 Explanations
	Multiplication and Division of Integers	Activities 3.5	Chapter 3 Explanations
	Divisibility	Activities 4.7-4.8	Chapter 4 Explanations
	Prime and Composite Numbers	Activities 4.1-4.4	Chapter 4 Explanations
	Greatest Common Divisor and Least Common Multiple	Activity 4.9	Chapter 4 Explanations
	Clock and Modular Arithmetic	Activities 4.10-4.12	Chapter 4 Explanations
		Additional Items: Activities 4.5-4.6 that explore special types of primes; Activities 4.13-4.16 that explore ways of representing number theory ideas and proofs	*Additional Items:* Historical/Social/ Cultural Notes on Number Theory
Rational Numbers as Fractions	The Set of Rational Numbers	Activity 7.14	Chapter 6 Explanations
	Addition and Subtraction of Rational Numbers	Activities 6.12-6.14	Chapter 6 Explanations
	Multiplication and Division of Rational Numbers	Activities 6.12-6.16	Chapter 6 Explanations
		Additional Items: Activities 6.1-6.8, 6.10-6.11 that explore three models to represent fractions; Activity 6.9 that explores the density of the set of real numbers	*Additional Items:* Historical/Social/ Cultural Notes on Fractions
Exponents and Decimals	Integer Exponents and Decimals	Activity 7.4	Chapter 7 Explanations
	Operations on Decimals	Activities 7.6-7.7	Chapter 7 Explanations
	Real Numbers	Activities 7.12-7.14	Chapter 7 Explanations
		Additional Items: Activity 7.5 that explores why the decimal point placement rules work	*Additional Items:* Historical/Social/ Cultural Notes on Rationals and Irrationals

Applications of Mathematics	Algebraic Thinking	Activities 8.5-8.8, 8.12-8.13	Chapter 8 Explanations
	Word Problems	Activities 8.1-8.10	Chapter 8 Explanations
	Lines in a Cartesian Coordinate System	Activity 10.13	Chapter 8 Explanations; Chapter 10 Explanations
	Ratio and Proportion	Activities 7.1-7.3	Chapter 7 Explanations
	Percents	Activities 7.8-7.11	Chapter 7 Explanations
	Computing Interest	Activity 8.10	Chapter 8 Explanations
		Additional Items: Activities 8.9, 8.11 that explore iterated functions; Activity 8.14 that explores distance versus time motion	
Probability	How Probabilities are Determined	Activity 5.5	Chapter 5 Explanations
	Multistage Experiments with Tree Diagrams and Geometric Probabilities	Activities 5.1-3	Chapter 5 Explanations
	Using Simulations in Probability		
	Odds and Expected Value	Activity 5.5	Chapter 5 Explanations
	Methods of Counting	Activity 5.6	Chapter 5 Explanations
		Additional Items: Activity 5.4 that explores fairness	*Additional Items:* Historical/Social/Cultural Notes on Probability
Statistics	Statistical Graphs	Activities 5.7-5.10	Chapter 5 Explanations
	Measures of Central Tendency and Variation	Activity 5.8	Chapter 5 Explanations
	Normal Distributions	Activity 5.7	
	Abuses of Statistics	Activity 5.11	Chapter 5 Explanations
			Additional Items: Historical/Social/Cultural Notes on Statistics

Introductory Geometry	Basic Notions	Activity 9.3	Chapter 9 Explanations
	Polygonal Curves	Activities 9.7-9.10	Chapter 9 Explanations
	Linear Measure	Activities 9.5, 9.11, 10.1-10.4	Chapter 10 Explanations
	More about Angles	Activities 9.6	Chapter 9 Explanations
	Geometry in Three Dimensions	Activity 10.10	Chapter 10 Explanations
	Networks		
		Additional Items: Activities 9.1-9.2 that explore the importance of precision of language	*Additional Items:* Historical/Social/ Cultural Notes on Geometry
Constructions and Similarity	Congruence through Constructions	Activity 9.4	Chapter 9 Explanations
	Other Congruence Properties	Activities 9.12	Chapter 9 Explanations
	Other Constructions	Activity 9.4	
	Similar Triangles and Similar Figures	Activity 9. 13-9.14	Chapter 9 Explanations
	Trigonometry Ratios via Similarity		
		Additional Items: Activities 9.15-9.16 that explores proving geometry ideas; Activity 9.17 that explores spherical geometry	*Additional Items:* Historical/Social/ Cultural Notes on Geometry
More Concepts of Measurement	Areas of Polygons and Circles	Activities 10.2-10.3, 10.6, 10.8	Chapter 10 Explanations
	The Pythagorean Theorem	Activity 10.5	
	Surface Areas	Activities 10.9, 10.11	Chapter 10 Explanations
	Volumes	Activities 10.9, 10.12	Chapter 10 Explanations
	Mass and Temperature		
		Additional Items: Activity 10.7 that explores the circumference to diameter ratio	*Additional Items:* Historical/Social/ Cultural Notes on Measurement

Motion Geometry and Tessellations	Translations and Rotations	Activities 10.14-10.15	Chapter 10 Explanations
	Reflections and Glide Reflections	Activity 10.16	Chapter 10 Explanations
	Size Transformations		
	Symmetries		Chapter 10 Exercises & More Problems
	Tessellations of the Plane	Activities 10.17-10.18	Chapter 10 Explanations
			Additional Items: Historical/Social/ Cultural Notes on Measurement

Chapter 0: Learning Mathematics via Problem Solving

Chapter Overview:

Mathematics instruction has changed rather dramatically in recent years. A passive transmission view of the teacher's role has been replaced by one involving students as active participants in the act of "doing" mathematics. This new vision is one where mathematics is seen as a cooperative venture in which students are encouraged to explore, make and debate conjectures, build connections among concepts, solve problems growing out of their explorations, and construct personal meaning from all of these experiences.

This chapter provides a discussion of the philosophy underlying teaching and learning "via problem solving." Also included are brief discussions of key ingredients of the materials contained in the *Activity Book*, namely: the importance of emphasizing big mathematical ideas, cooperative learning, reflective writing, alternative assessment, and different classroom roles for both instructors and students.

Chapter Outline:

The Changing Nature of Mathematics Instruction

The Role of Problem Solving in Instruction
    Teaching About Problem Solving
    Teaching For Problem Solving
    Teaching Via Problem Solving

Important Ingredients of the Activities in the Activity Book
    "Big Ideas" in Mathematics for Prospective Elementary Teachers
    Cooperative Learning
    Reflective Writing
    Assessment: Emphases and Practices
    *Instructor's and Students' Roles in Learning Mathematics Via
        Problem Solving*

Bibliography

THE CHANGING NATURE OF MATHEMATICS INSTRUCTION

Mathematics instruction has changed rather dramatically in recent years. In the past, mathematics instruction was viewed by many as an activity in which an "expert" attempted to transmit her or his knowledge of mathematics to a group of mostly passive students, typically by means of lectures. This passive transmission view has been replaced by one involving students as active participants in the act of "doing"—that is, creating, exploring, testing, verifying, etc.—mathematics. This new vision is one where mathematics is seen as a cooperative venture in which students are encouraged to explore, make and debate conjectures, build connections among concepts, solve problems growing out of their explorations, and construct personal meaning from all of these experiences.

The emphasis in the activities in this book is on learning mathematical concepts and processes by doing mathematics and, in particular, by solving problems. Also, this active doing of mathematics takes place in an environment of cooperation among small groups of students in which the teachers plays the roles of guide, coach, question asker, and co-problem solver.

THE ROLE OF PROBLEM SOLVING IN MATHEMATICS INSTRUCTION

Most mathematics educators agree that problem solving is a very important, if not the most important, goal of mathematics instruction at every level. Indeed, some have even gone so far as to insist that: "Problem solving should be the focus of school mathematics" (National Council of Teachers of Mathematics [NCTM], 1980, p. 1), and "Problem solving is a central focus of the mathematics curriculum" (Mathematical Sciences Education Board, 1990, p. 31). Since about 1980, problem solving has been the most written about topic in the mathematics curriculum in the United States. And, most teachers agree that the development of students' problem-solving abilities is a primary objective of instruction.

The question arises: "How can we make problem solving the focus of mathematics instruction?" We have found it useful to think about the answer to this question by distinguishing among three approaches to problem-solving instruction: (a) teaching *about* problem solving, (b) teaching *for* problem solving, and (c) teaching *via* problem solving. (See the article, "Developing Understanding in Mathematics via Problem Solving," in the 1989 yearbook of the National Council of Teachers of Mathematics for a more thorough discussion of these three approaches to problem-solving instruction; Schroeder & Lester, 1989).

Teaching *About* Problem Solving

The teacher who teaches *about* problem solving emphasizes the various phases or stages that are involved in the process of solving mathematics problems. The best known model of this sort was proposed by the eminent mathematician, George Polya, more than 50 years ago (Polya, 1945). Briefly, Polya's model describes a set of four interdependent phases that are involved in the process of solving mathematics problems: understanding the problem, devising a plan, carrying out the plan, and looking back. Teachers who teach *about* problem solving encourage their students to use the phases, which according to Polya, expert problem solvers use when solving mathematics problems. These teachers also encourage their students to become aware of their own progression through these phases when they themselves solve problems. Additionally, they are taught a number of "heuristics" or "strategies" from which they can choose and which they should use in devising and carrying out their problem-solving plans. Some of the several strategies typically taught include: looking for patterns, solving a simpler problem, and working backwards. Teaching *about* problem solving usually includes experiences actually solving problems, but it always almost involves a great deal of discussion of the problem-solving process and teaching about how problems are solved.

Teaching *For* Problem Solving

Teachers who choose to teach *for* problem solving are interested in teaching so that the mathematics being taught can be applied in the solution of both routine and non-routine problems. The teacher interested in teaching *for* problem solving thinks the primary purpose for learning mathematics is to be able to use it. Consequently, students are exposed to many examples of mathematical concepts and structures and given many opportunities to apply mathematics in solving problems. Further, teachers who teach *for* problem solving are very concerned about their students' ability to transfer what they have learned from one problem context to others. A strong believer in this approach would suggest that the primary reason for learning mathematics is to be able to use the knowledge gained to solve problems.

Teaching *via* Problem Solving

In teaching *via* problem solving, problems are used not only for their value in helping students learn mathematics, but also as the primary means for doing so. Adherents of this approach begin instruction on a mathematical topic with a problem situation that embodies key aspects of the topic, and mathematical techniques are developed as sensible methods to use to solve problems. The learning of mathematics in this way may be viewed as a development from the concrete (a "real world" problem which serves as an instance of the mathematical concept or technique) to the abstract (a symbolic representation of a class of problems, and techniques for operating with that representation).

Unlike the other two approaches, until recently teaching *via* problem solving was a conception that had not been adopted by many teachers. But, teaching *via* problem solving is the approach that is most consistent with the recommendation of the NCTM *Standards* that: (a) mathematics concepts and skills be learned in the context of solving problems; (b) the development of higher level thinking processes be fostered through problem-solving experiences; and (c) mathematics instruction take place in an inquiry-oriented, problem-solving atmosphere (NCTM, 1989).

The materials included in the *Activity Book* and the *Resource Manual* have been designed with four main goals in mind:

1. To help students develop adult-level perspective and insights into the nature of mathematics taught in the elementary school;
2. To improve students' ability to engage in mathematical thinking and reasoning;
3. To increase students' ability to use their mathematical knowledge to solve problems; and
4. To expose students to learning mathematics via problem solving.

[Additional references: Lester & Mau (1993), Lester et al. (1994)]

IMPORTANT INGREDIENTS OF THE ACTIVITIES IN THE *ACTIVITY BOOK*

Five features characterize the activities: (1) *"big mathematical ideas"* serve as important organizers for the course; (2) *cooperative learning* is an essential part of regular instruction; (3) *reflective writing* is considered a useful tool to help students make strong connections among the mathematical ideas they encounter and consolidate their mathematical understanding; (4) *assessment* is a continuous activity engaged in by both the teacher and students to the extent that it becomes a natural part of instruction; and (5) the new view of instruction requires that both the *teacher and students assume different roles* in daily classroom activities.

"Big Ideas" in Mathematics for Prospective Elementary Teachers

The term "big idea" refers to those themes that pervade several areas of mathematics and which serve to make connections among mathematics topics. These big ideas, then, are recurring, unifying themes in mathematics. With respect to identifying KEY big ideas to emphasize in the activities, we decided that to be a big idea an idea should:

1. Help students make connections among what may for them seem like unrelated topics;
2. Help students make connections between the world of mathematics and the real, everyday world, and
3. Provide ample opportunities for students to develop a greater appreciation for and understanding of the beauty of mathematics and mathematical activity.

Notwithstanding our belief that it is not so important to be concerned about selecting a specific set of themes, it is useful to take a look at what others think the big ideas in mathematics are. In particular, we found three books to be especially helpful: *The Mathematical Experience* (Davis & Hersh, 1981), *On the Shoulders of Giants* (Steen, 1990), and *The Growth of Mathematical Ideas: Grades K - 12* (NCTM, 1959). A brief overview of each of these books illustrates how the authors think about big mathematical ideas.

The Mathematical Experience. The authors of this powerful treatise on the nature of mathematics and mathematical activity, Philip Davis and Reuben Hersh, identify both inner and outer issues related to doing and studying mathematics. Their outer issues have to do with the utility of mathematics. Their inner issues seem to be closest to our notion of big ideas. They are as follows: abstraction, aesthetics, algorithmic vs. dialectic mathematics, formalization, generalization, infinity, math objects & structures, pattern, order & chaos, proof, symbolism, and unification.

On the Shoulders of Giants. The authors of this widely-read book on the nature of contemporary mathematics discuss two types of ideas: *connective themes* and *deep ideas* (that nourish the branches of mathematics). Both types seem to be related to our view of big ideas. Their *connective themes* include: algorithms, classification, exploration, inference, measurement, symmetry, and visualization. Their deep ideas include the notions of: mathematical structures, attributes, actions, abstractions, attitudes, behaviors, and dichotomies.

The Growth of Mathematical Ideas: Grades K - 12. The authors of the 24th yearbook of the NCTM insisted that "teachers . . . plan so that pupils continually have recurring but varied contacts with the fundamental ideas and processes of mathematics" (p. 2). Their list of big ideas includes the following: language & symbolism, mathematical modes of thought, measurement & approximation, number & operation, probability, proof, relations & functions, and statistics.

Some Thoughts about Big Ideas

Of course, each of the authors considered above used somewhat different terminology, but there was considerable agreement that the number of truly big ideas is relatively small. Moreover, it is interesting to note that traditional branches of mathematics (e. g., algebra, geometry, calculus) were not viewed by any of the authors as being big ideas in themselves and mathematical "actions" seemed to be as important as mathematical "structures."

Our own thinking, guided by a consideration of the ideas expressed in the three volumes mentioned above, has led to a conceptualization of the big ideas in terms of three dimensions: *structures, actions*, and *tactics*. Each dimension contains big ideas that exemplify a fundamental theme, process, or aim of mathematical activity.

Structures include mathematical ideas and entities such as equivalence, function & relation, measurement, number & operation, shape & space, and pattern & order, among others. The structures identified here are almost arbitrary; many other (perhaps better) structures could have been chosen. This is consistent with the notion that the specific big ideas are not nearly as important for these courses as the idea that there are unifying themes that pervade many branches of mathematics.

The *actions* refer to the sorts of activities that individuals engage in when they are doing mathematics and, as often as not, they are the goals of mathematical activity (e.g., creating a generalization, developing a useful mathematical model). These actions help distinguish mathematical activity from other kinds of intellectual activity. Among the actions that seem to be particularly relevant for courses for prospective teachers are verifying, generalizing, modeling, representing, and composing/decomposing.

The *tactics* dimension includes tools that help the individual do mathematics. More specifically, tactics assist the person doing mathematics in implementing mathematical *actions*. The four tactics we have chosen are conjecturing, creating & using algorithms, using problem-solving strategies, and developing & using appropriate language and symbolism, but there may be other equally as important tactics.

Finally, we reiterate the tentative, incomplete nature of these dimensions and the big ideas contained within them. However, they provided a framework for us in our development of the activities and materials in the *Activity Book* and *Resource Manual*. Samples of big ideas within each of the three dimensions are shown in Table 1. [*Note*: Big ideas associated with each chapter of the *Activity Book* are identified at the beginning of each chapter in the chapter overview.]

Table 1
Sample Big Ideas in Mathematics

Structures	Actions	Tactics
Equivalence	Generalizing	Creating/using algorithms
Function/relation	Representing	Conjecturing
Measurement	(De)composing	Using heuristics
Number & operation	Verifying	Using language & symbolism
Shape & space	Modeling	

Cooperative Learning

The philosophy behind the appropriate use of the materials in the *Activity Book* requires that students—rather than the teacher— must bear the primary burden for making sense of mathematical ideas, for constructing mathematical arguments, and for providing mathematical explanations. Shifting the burden in this way is accomplished by organizing each class session in a very different way from the usual university mathematics class: During much of each class period students work cooperatively in small groups to wrestle with problems that challenge them, to develop new and deeper understandings of fundamental mathematical concepts, and to talk about their new ways of thinking.

On the first day of class the instructor should group students into cooperative groups of about four students each. Since most students will not yet know each other, typically initial groups are formed by merely suggesting that four students who are sitting near one another put their desks together for small-group work. Students are then expected to keep working each day with the same group of people until the teacher indicates that it is time for a change of groups (usually every 3 or 4 weeks).

When the time comes, some instructors find it best to form new groups totally at random. One way to do this is to put a pile of playing cards near the door and to instruct students to take a card as they arrive at class on the day when groups are to be changed. Then those four who have the same card number (for example, 7 or 2 or Queen), regardless of suit, form a group. Of course, the instructor will have to take extra cards out of the deck ahead of time so that the appropriate number of groups of four cards remain—for example, if there are 24 students in the class, an instructor might remove from the deck all cards except those from Ace through 6. This will leave 24 cards, six sets of four cards each.

There may be times when random assignment to groups does not seem appropriate. For example, if there are one or two students in a class who have trouble working together, the instructor may want to assign groups so that these students are separated. Or the instructor may want to arrange groups so that neither the best students (nor the weakest students) are concentrated in one group. Near the end of the semester, an instructor may choose to ask each student to turn in a list of individuals they would like to work with and may form groups deliberately to include students who have expressed an interest in working together.

The role of the instructor in class is quite different from in more traditional mathematics classes. Rather than preparing a lecture, the instructor is usually responsible for a three-part lesson: (a) providing a brief introduction to the day's activities, (b) circulating about the room while students work in small groups and making appropriate comments to the groups, (c) leading wrap-up whole-class discussions where various groups share their thinking about the problem and the instructor helps everyone consolidate their thinking about their work. [This type of wrap-up often occurs several times throughout the class period, as well as at the end of each class.]

Before students begin work in their groups, the instructor should talk briefly to the entire class, introducing the activity of the day, explaining any new terminology or special instructions, and indicating how this activity fits into the larger context of the course. Note that this introduction is not a time for telling how to solve the problem at hand: **Solving the problem is the task of the students working in their small groups.** Students will probably be frustrated at first with small group work because they are accustomed to being told by their teachers exactly what to do. By contrast, the problem-solving activities challenge students to do their own thinking and the instructor's role is merely to introduce the activity and to guide students to discover their own solutions.

As the instructor circulates around the room while students are working in small groups, he or she must assume the role of question asker, problem poser, and careful listener; the students are the problem solvers and explainers, not the instructor. No matter how many times the instructor tells the students that *they* must be the problem solvers, they will only believe it if the instructor demonstrates it by his or her actions in the classroom. Four tenets should guide the instructor's behaviors:

- *Don't be an answer giver.* Try not to provide right/wrong judgments or to tell students how to proceed on a problem. If you do, they will always be waiting for you to tell them the next time, instead of thinking for themselves. If students ask, "Is this right?" ask them how they might decide for themselves. Some appropriate replies are "What do your group members think?" or "Can you find another way to verify your answer?"

- *De-emphasize correct answers.* Try to help students understand that you are more interested in depth of understanding, in ability to communicate mathematical ideas clearly, and in reasonable thinking than simply in correct answers. As you move from group to group, avoid asking "What did you get?" Instead ask questions that require explanation such as "Can you tell me what you've been thinking?" or "What strategies have you been using to approach this problem?"

- *Be prepared with appropriate hints.* There is more than one way to solve nearly every problem. When students are stuck, the instructor may need to provide a hint, but the hint should build on whatever progress the group has already made. For example, if students have been experimenting with specific numbers, it might be appropriate to suggest organizing findings in a table so that a pattern may become more apparent. If students are stuck because a problem has very large numbers or seems too complicated, it might be good to suggest trying some simpler cases first. It is usually not appropriate to provide a hint that merely provides students with the first (or a subsequent) step in a problem solution because this is often tantamount to telling students how to solve the problem.

- *Be prepared with problem extensions.* Some groups in the classroom will work faster than others. The experienced instructor helps these students (and eventually all students) to think beyond the task at hand. For example, it is often useful to ask students how they would solve the problem if conditions were changed (numbers different, question different, more constraints, etc.) or to ask them if they can work from their specific solution to a solution for a generalization of the problem.

One of the most important parts of the class is the wrap-up discussion that takes place after small groups have worked on problems. Once again, the instructor must guard against playing too prominent a role. There is no point in telling the class how their groups should have solved the problem. An instructor who does this will find that groups soon have no motivation to work on their own: Why should students struggle to work a problem if they know the teacher will explain it later? The wrap-up discussion should be a session where all groups have a chance to tell what approaches they tried, how successful or unsuccessful they were, and what conclusions they drew from their efforts. The best discussions are those in which the students do most of the talking—comparing approaches, arguing, and trying to convince one another of the validity of their findings. The instructor's role is to orchestrate this discussion so that everyone has an opportunity to participate, so that everyone can hear and understand what others are saying, and so that some closure is reached by the end of the discussion. Although it is important to allow everyone to contribute (even those whose solutions are incorrect), it is also important not to leave students hanging at the end, uncertain as to what makes sense and what doesn't. At the end of an ideal problem discussion, students will have reached their own conclusions about the validity of various problem solutions and will have a good sense of how the day's work fits into the bigger picture of the mathematical concepts being studied in the course.

[Additional References: Davidson, 1990; EQUALS, 1989; Weissglass, 1990]

Reflective Writing

Reflective thinking occurs both inside and outside the classroom. Inside the classroom, students reflect as they work to understand a problem, evaluate their solution processes, decide if their solutions make sense, justify their generalizations, connect mathematical concepts, understand a problem solution different from their own, extend a problem, monitor their thinking processes, and communicate their ideas to other students and the teacher. When students are encouraged and expected to be reflective in their work, they become better at thinking reflectively, their understanding of the content improves, they are more creative and insightful in their problem solving, their motivation for learning increases, and they begin to look for, and make, connections between mathematical concepts (Borasi & Rose, 1989).

Outside of the classroom students can continue their reflective activity through reflective writing. Reflective writing benefits students in four ways: (a) therapeutic value, (b) increased learning of content, (c) improvements in learning and problem-solving skills, and (d) change in one's conception of mathematics. Reflective thinking and writing are meaning-making processes that involve the student in actively building connections between what they are learning and what they already know.

In general, there are two broad types of reflective writing assignments that are used to give students the opportunity to reflect on their feelings and thoughts and communicate these in written form. The first type is an assignment that encourages the students to come to terms with their feelings and beliefs about mathematics. Some examples of this type are as follows:

- Write a brief description of your thinking as you played the games "Poison" and "What's My Number?"
- Discuss how you think mathematics fits with the real world. How do you think new mathematics is created? Has this changed your definition of mathematics?

The second type of reflective writing assignment asks the students to explain a mathematical idea or procedure. It forces the students to ask themselves, "Do I really understand this?" Several examples of open-ended assignments of this type are listed below.

- Explain why the Sieve of Eratosthenes works, in general, in identifying prime numbers.
- What do you consider to be the three most important features of a numeration system? Why?
- Verification is a big mathematical idea. What is the essence of this idea and why is it so important?

Throughout the course the reflective writing provides a record of the student's development through time, which provides new awareness and stimulus for reflection. This record also allows the teacher to enter into a dialogue with the student by responding to, challenging, and encouraging reflectiveness.

Assessment: Emphases and Practices

Assessment is perhaps the most worrisome aspect of any mathematics course for both the instructor and students, due in part to the fact that assessment is commonly associated (often exclusively) with grading and in part to the all-too-often mysterious nature of the instructor's assessment practices. We encourage the instructor to explain carefully to the students the various sources of data to be used for grading. These sources of data might include class participation, tests and quizzes, homework, reflective writing, and group projects. From the confluence of these data sources, the instructor assigns each student a grade that indicates the extent to which he or she has reached the goal of the course, namely, to develop good understanding of key mathematical ideas and to be able to communicate these ideas clearly and efficiently to others.

Assessment Is Not Just a Matter of Grading

Yet instructors should not think of assessment only in terms of assigning grades. Another just as important reason for assessment is to help the instructor build an accurate mental picture of the understandings held by students and to enable him or her to adjust instruction accordingly. Thus, assessment is an ongoing process in the classroom. For example, whenever the instructor is circulating throughout the room during small group work, he or she should be assessing the progress of the various groups, trying to get a picture of student understandings, and making mental plans so that the wrap-up discussion or the next class session may be orchestrated to help students deepen their understandings. Another source of assessment data for the instructor is the students' reflective writing. By reading students' writing, an instructor gets additional insight into which topics have been understood and which need more attention or a more focused discussion.

Still another reason for assessment is to indicate to students what is considered important. Because being able to communicate about mathematics is an important goal of the course, instructors must allow sufficient time for students to talk about mathematics and to write about it. And they must offer thoughtful reactions to students' communicative efforts, so that the students can see that their efforts to explain their ideas are valued.

Recommended Assessment Practices

Because teaching via problem solving requires a different type of instructional approach and different expectations of students, it also demands new ways of assessing student growth. In particular, it requires using more than just tests and quizzes for assessment. For example, if one accepts the position that assessment should be embedded in classroom work and should be aligned with classroom methods, then it makes sense that group assessment would be used in a class where group problem solving is the norm. A second reason for using alternative assessment techniques is that use of a variety of methods can provide a much richer vision of what students think, believe, and know than that obtained from any single method alone. Finally, in a course for prospective teachers, it is especially important that use of alternative assessment be modeled. As a result of a dozen or more years of schooling, many college students have developed the notion that the most important forms of assessment provide grades and serve to differentiate students from their peers. However, we would like to develop prospective teachers who have a broader view of assessment—who understand that, in the long run, grades are less important than how an individual's understanding is being deepened. Let us consider some alternative assessment techniques that we have used successfully. See Lambdin Kroll, Masingila & Mau (1992), Lester & Lambdin Kroll (1991), Mathematical Sciences Education Board (1993), and Stenmark (1991) for considerably more information about alternative assessment in mathematics classes.

Classroom Observation and Interaction. Classroom observation and interaction can be used as an alternative form of assessment. If students solve problems and discuss mathematical ideas in small groups, an instructor can watch and listen carefully while circulating from group to group. From a compilation of such observations, a more complete picture of students' understandings can be constructed than from any batch of test papers—and, as a result, more appropriate decisions concerning future instruction can be made.

Instructors can also gain important insights about the climate in their classroom as they interact with small groups of students: Are students confident? Frustrated? Involved? What beliefs about mathematics are being fostered by the work that students are doing? It is important to take time to think about how students feel and what they believe about the mathematics they are learning. Furthermore, when an instructor poses thought-provoking questions to a group of students working together, and demands responses that provide clear explanations of students' reasoning, students soon learn the importance of considering *why* mathematics makes sense rather than focusing solely on answers. They begin to appreciate the necessity of being able to communicate using precise mathematical language. Thus, the use of observation and interaction as assessment tools not only benefits the instructor, but also helps students develop an appreciation for what is really important in the learning and teaching of mathematics—an appreciation that is particularly important if the students are prospective teachers who are, themselves, to become reflective practitioners.

Although the use of a variety of assessment techniques helps instructors make decisions and aids in communicating expectations to students, it is also true that a major reason for assessing student work is to judge progress and assign grades. Grades in our mathematics course for teachers are based in part on sources that sound like they would be quite traditional (e.g., quizzes, tests, and class participation), and in part on other, more obviously non-traditional aspects of the course such as group presentations, written reflections, and concept maps. Yet, even quizzes and tests may need to be assessed in new and different ways, when the methods of teaching are non-traditional.

Group Problem Solving during Tests. The NCTM *Standards* stress the importance of aligning assessment techniques with teaching methods. Since so much class time will involve students working in cooperative groups, tests should consist of both an individual component and a group problem solving component. The group portion of each test involves two phases. In phase one, students work in small (pre-assigned) groups to solve a problem and to write a single group solution. In phase two, individuals are expected—on their own—to be able to answer individual questions about the group's solution and to solve problem extensions. (See Lambdin Kroll, Masingila & Mau, 1992, for a detailed description of how cooperative work on tests can be graded.)

Having a group portion on each test emphasizes to students several underlying messages of the course: that mathematics is not a solitary endeavor, that there are a variety of alternative approaches to problems, and that clarity of communication is important. Moreover, group problem solving provides an opportunity for students of every ability level to work together and to contribute to a common goal. Assessment of problem solving in groups also makes the point that prospective teachers need to consider themselves responsible not only for their own learning, but also for that of the others in the group. They should already consider themselves teachers in training.

Group Presentations and Group Projects. Another source of assessment data can be provided by group projects and presentations. In working on group projects outside of class, we have found that many students—for the first time—find themselves doing mathematics without continuous monitoring by a teacher. After having worked cooperatively to complete a project, students are expected to communicate to their peers and their instructor (in a group report to the class and in individual written reflections) their own self assessments of the mathematics concepts they used and the difficulties they encountered in accomplishing the project. In their presentation to the class, students must, in a professional manner, explain concepts and field questions about their mathematical thinking in the task. Thus, group presentations provide instructors with new layers to add to their multidimensional assessment of students' understanding, as well as providing students with still another situation where they must engage in reflection and self assessment.

Notebooks: Reflective Writing, Class and Homework Activities. Prospective teachers in our mathematics classes keep a notebook that contains a variety of documents including activities from the *Activity Book*, homework assignments and quizzes, as well reflective writing assignments. The notebooks serve two assessment functions: they help students become more aware of their own strengths and weaknesses, and they provide an avenue for confidential one-to-one communication with the instructor.

Instructor's and Students' Roles in Learning Mathematics via Problem Solving
As we mentioned earlier in this chapter, the instructor's role in a course emphasizing learning mathematics via problem solving is drastically different from the role he or she assumes in a more traditional, lecture-based course.

Students' must accept different roles also! No longer are they allowed to sit passively and simply "absorb" information transmitted to them by the instructor. Students are expected to listen to, respond to, and question the teacher and one another. They should also be reflective thinkers to become aware of how they themselves learn mathematics. Validity of particular representations and solutions should be determined by mathematical evidence and argument, whether working in large or small groups, and not by seeking the "right" answer from the teacher. It is probably inevitable, then, that some student frustration will arise in this environment because of prior student beliefs about the nature of mathematics and expectations about the proper role of the teacher. It is ultimately the task of the student to try to make sense of her or his mathematical experiences.

We realize, however, that role changes of this sort are not easy to make. One reason for the difficulty is that many instructors feel comfortable being "in charge" (of both the content to be taught and the students) and may have painstakingly developed lecture notes over the years that they are loath to give up. There is also the matter of the teacher needing to learn how to adopt an appropriate balance, sensing when to intervene and re-direct student exploration and when to allow the student to stumble along. A teacher who gives detailed directions may be sending the message that students are to be dependent on her for all knowledge. But a teacher who gives almost no direction increases the possibility of student frustrations rising to a debilitating level. Thus, the teacher's role is that of a guide, not that of an authority. The teacher chooses which problems and activities to use as a means for introducing material and guides the discussion of these problems, but the teacher does not pronounce solutions. This is fundamentally different from what has been considered appropriate teacher behavior in the past.

At the same time, college students have experienced years of training in which the teacher was the authority and the teacher's word was as close to the "truth" as was possible. As a result, many college students expect the teacher to tell them what to learn and how to learn it. That is, they have not developed autonomous learning behaviors that they will one day hope to develop in the children they will teach.

A heavy reliance on cooperative learning removes the teacher as the authority figure and minimizes the possibility of students blindly emulating the teacher's modeled techniques and solutions. Students are forced into helping each other develop their own deeper understanding of mathematical principles and mathematical autonomous learning behaviors.

The overarching responsibility of the teacher is to establish a mathematical community in the classroom where everyone's thinking is respected and in which reasoning and discussing mathematical ideas and meanings is the norm. Within this community, the teacher's insightful questioning can play an important role in stimulating student thinking so that there are opportunities for students to examine and question their beliefs about mathematics, to have their misconceptions challenged, and to seek clarifications, strategies, and verifications without direct teacher intervention.

The traditional mathematics classroom is teacher-centered. In a typical teacher-centered class, the first activity is for the teacher to check answers for the previous day's assignment. Second, the more difficult problems are worked by the teacher or students at the chalkboard. Then, a brief explanation is given by the teacher of any new material and problems (exercises) are assigned for the next day. The remainder of class is devoted to working on homework while the teacher is available for answering questions. This type of instruction implies that there is a specific mathematical knowledge that the teacher has and through modeling what the teacher does and through passive absorption, students will acquire this knowledge.

In summary, a course following a learning via problem solving approach requires new and different roles for both instructors and students, roles that are negotiated throughout the semester. Table 2 contrasts a course emphasizing learning via problem solving with a traditional college mathematics course.

Table 2
Contrast Between a Traditional Approach and a Learning via Problem Solving Approach

Approach to College Mathematics Instruction	
Traditional Approach	**Learning via Problem Solving Approach**
Teacher's Role	
	• Guides and facilitates
• Lectures	
• Assigns seat work	• Poses challenging questions
• Dispenses knowledge	• Helps students share knowledge
Student's Role	
• Works individually	• Works in a group
• Learns passively	• Learns actively
• Forms mainly "weak" constructions	• Forms mainly "strong" constructions

BIBLIOGRAPHY

Davidson, N. (Ed.). (1990). *Cooperative learning in mathematics: A handbook for teachers.* Menlo Park, CA: Addison-Wesley.

Davis, P. J., & Hersh, R. (1981). *The mathematical experience.* Boston: Birkhäuser.

EQUALS. (1989). *Get it together: Math problems for groups—grades 4 - 12.* Berkeley, CA: Lawrence Hall of Science.

Johnson, D.W., & Johnson, R.T. (1990). Using cooperative learning in math. In N. Davidson (Ed.), *Cooperative learning in mathematics* (pp. 103-125). Menlo Park, Ca: Addison-Wesley Publishing Company.

Lambdin Kroll, D., Masingila, J. O., & Mau, S. M. (1992). Cooperative problem solving: But what about grading? *Arithmetic Teacher, 39*(6), 17-23.

Lester, F. K., & Lambdin Kroll, D. (1991). Implementing the Standards—Evaluation: A new vision. *Mathematics Teacher,* 84(4), 276-284.

Lester, F. K., Masingila, J. O., Mau, S. T., Lambdin Kroll, D., Santos, V. P., & Raymond, A. M. (1994). Learning how to teach via problem solving. In D. A. Aichele (Ed.), *The professional development of teachers of mathematics.* 1994 yearbook of the National Council of Teachers of Mathematics. Reston, VA: NCTM.

Lester, F. K., & Mau, S. T. (1993). Teaching mathematics via problem solving: A course for elementary teachers. *For the Learning of Mathematics, 13*(1).

Mathematical Sciences Education Board/National Research Council. (1990). *Reshaping school mathematics: A philosophy and framework for curriculum.* Washington, D. C.: National Academy Press.

Mathematical Sciences Education Board/National Research Council. (1993). *Measuring up: Prototypes for mathematics assessment.* Washington, DC: National Academy Press.

National Council of Teachers of Mathematics. (1959). *The growth of mathematical ideas K - 12.* (24th yearbook of the Council). Reston, VA: Author.

National Council of Teachers of Mathematics. (1980). *An agenda for action: Recommendations for school mathematics for the 1980s.* Reston, VA: Author.

National Council of Teachers of Mathematics. (1989). *Curriculum and evaluation standards for school mathematics.* Reston, VA: Author.

Polya, G. (1945). *How to solve it.* (2nd ed.). Princeton, NJ: Princeton University Press.

Schroeder, T. L., & Lester, F. K. (1989). Developing understanding in mathematics via problem solving. In P. R. Trafton (Ed.), *New directions for elementary school mathematics* (1989 Yearbook of the National Council of Teachers of Mathematics) (pp. 31-42). Reston, VA: NCTM.

Steen, L. A. (Ed.). (1990). *On the shoulders of giants: New approaches to numeracy.* Washington, DC: National Academy Press.

Stenmark, J. K. (Ed.) (1991). *Mathematics assessment: Myths, models, good questions, and practical suggestions.* Reston, VA: National Council of Teachers of Mathematics.

Weissglass, J. (1990). *Exploring elementary mathematics: A small-group approach for teaching.* Dubuque, IA: Kendall/Hunt.

Chapter 1: Getting Started in Learning Mathematics via Problem Solving

Chapter Overview:

In this chapter you will begin to see just how different this course is from any other mathematics course you have taken. The activities in this chapter focus on three things: (1) learning how to *work in a small, cooperative group* on real mathematical investigations, (2) becoming *less dependent on your instructor* for answers and direction, and (3) learning about certain key *problem-solving strategies*. All of this will be done in the context of playing various strategy games and exploring solutions to some interesting problems. Throughout the activities you will be gaining valuable experience in how to collaborate in a productive way with others without relying on your instructor. You will also be looking for patterns, guessing and checking, making conjectures, using logical reasoning, and making organized lists.

Big Mathematical Ideas:

> problem-solving strategies, generalizing, verifying, using language & symbolism

NCTM Standards Links:

> *K - 4:*   Mathematics as problem solving; Mathematics as reasoning; Mathematical connections; Patterns & relationships
>
> *5 - 8:*   Mathematics as problem solving; Mathematics as reasoning; Mathematical connections; Patterns & functions

Chapter Outline:

Notes 1.1—What's My Number?

MATH CONTENT

- Numeration and place value

MATERIALS

- Paper to record information

CONNECTIONS

- Exercises and More Problems: #30
- Activity 1.2 ties in well with this activity and together these activities give students a good introduction to the course.

TIMETABLE

- 10 minutes for activity
- 10 minutes for group challenges and class discussion of strategies

ACTIVITY DISCUSSION

There are two purposes for beginning the course with some game-like activities: (1) they encourage group work, and (2) they illustrate the value of being *strategic* in problem solving. As the students play the game be sure to walk around the room and observe how they are thinking. Look for evidence of strategic play and sound logical reasoning. For "What's My Number?" also look for evidence that sensible records are being kept of guesses. An organized list will be helpful in keeping records. You may want to point our that the idea is to gain information from guesses, not to guess wildly (i.e., use the method of guess and check).

Suggestions for getting the game underway:
Form groups of 4 using some random assignment process (e.g., each student might be given a card with one of the numbers 1 through 8 on it as (s)he enters the room. All ones will be a group, etc.) Mention that group work will be an important part of this course and that a part of their grades will be determined on the basis of the extent to which they cooperated well with others in their group.

Announce: We are going to play a strategy game. In order to become expert at playing this game, you should look for general strategies to use. I will go over the rules of the game and then play a round or two with you to make sure that you understand how to play. Then, you will play the game in your groups. THE OBJECT IS FOR YOUR GROUP TO DETERMINE GOOD STRATEGIES FOR PLAYING THE GAME. Once you think you have a good strategy, you must be able to explain the logic of your strategy to everyone in your group. Then groups will challenge each other to test their strategies. Turn in your books to page 16 and read the directions for the game "What's My Number?"

Observe the students during the game playing and try to note strategies that they appear to be using. During the discussion of the game, ask the students to discuss what strategies they used and also mention those that you observed, if they were not mentioned by the students.

ACTIVITY SOLUTIONS

One key to playing this game efficiently is to recognize that you want to get as much new information per "guess" (i.e., turn) as possible. Try to eliminate digits and be sure to keep a record of all turns so that you can compare your most recent "guess" with previous guesses.

Notes 1.2—Poison

MATH CONTENT

- Algorithms

MATERIALS

- 10 color tiles per group

CONNECTIONS

- Exercises and More Problems: #28-29
- Activity 1.1 ties in well with this activity and together these activities give students a good introduction to the course.

TIMETABLE

- 10 minutes for activity
- 10 minutes for challenges and class discussion of strategies

ACTIVITY DISCUSSION

There are two purposes for beginning the course with some game-like activities: (1) they encourage group work, and (2) they illustrate the value of being *strategic* in problem solving. As the students play the game be sure to walk around the room and observe how they are thinking. Look for evidence of strategic play and sound logical reasoning. You may want to suggest that groups try starting with a different number of tiles (e.g., a smaller number) if they are struggling with generating strategies.

Have students read the directions for the game "Poison" and then play a round or two with the class to make sure the students understand how to play. Observe the students during the game playing and try to note strategies that they appear to be using. During the discussion of the game, ask the students to discuss what strategies they used and also mention those that you observed, if they were not mentioned by the students.

ACTIVITY SOLUTIONS

It is very unlikely that any group will come up with a generalized solution, like the one below, during class. Students should continue working on this outside of class and come to the next class period with their generalized solution.

If the number of tiles is of the form 3n, the 1st player takes two to win.
If the number of tiles is of the form 3n+1, the 2nd player wins no matter what player 1 does.
If the number of tiles is of the form 3n+2, the 1st player takes one to win.

Notes 1.3—Cereal Boxes and Patio Tiles

MATH CONTENT

- Arithmetic Patterns

MATERIALS

- 50 color tiles per group

CONNECTIONS

- Exercises and More Problems: #37

TIMETABLE

- 10-15 minutes for Problem 1
- 10-15 minutes for Problem 2
- 10 minutes for Problem 3
- 10 minutes for class discussion

ACTIVITY DISCUSSION

The purpose of this activity is to have students begin to look for patterns by solving several problems and to have them recognize that strategies used to solve one problem can be useful in solving another problem. Be aware that the students will generate creative solutions, particularly for the generalization of the cereal box problem. Insist that they verify their solutions. Students may not be able to arrive at a generalization for Part B until after working on Problem 2. If students seem to be thrown off (on Part B) by a number which does not seem to work (200 boxes), ask what they would have done in Part A if they had 48 boxes. Two strategies for arriving at the generalization follow. You may have to ask careful questions to guide the students in one of these directions.

Strategy 1: For the cereal box problem, the students will notice that consecutive integers are being summed. Thus,

$$\sum_{k=1}^{n} k = 1+2+3+ \ldots +n-2+n-1+n.$$

Pairing the numbers at each end we have:

$(1+n)+(2+n-1)+(3+n-2)+\ldots+(n-n/2+n-n/2+1)= (n+1)+(n+1)+(n+1)+\ldots+(n+1)$
[n/2 pairs of n+1] or $\sum k = (n/2)(n+1)$, if *n is even.*

If *n is odd*, the middle term will be $(n+1)/2$ and there will be $(n-1)/2$ pairs of n+1. That is, $\sum k = [(n-1)/2](n+1) + (n+1)/2 = (n/2)(n+1)$.

Strategy 2: Most students will arrive at the following conjecture for the patio tile problem: the middle row should have the number of tiles that is the square root of the largest square less than or equal to the total number of tiles. Using this conjecture, ask the students how the patio tiles might be arranged in a different configuration (viz., a square). Have the students verify this arrangement physically. The patio tile arrangement is two of the cereal box stacks minus one stack's bottom row. Two cereal box stacks could be arranged as a rectangle (square from the patio tile arrangement with the second bottom row added on). Looking at simple cases, the students can generate information like that below:

Bottom Row	Total Boxes	Double # Boxes	Rectangle
3	6	12	3x4
4	10	20	4x5
5	15	30	5x6
x	B	2B	x(x+1)

When the students start making conjectures about the rectangle for larger numbers of tiles, ask them to fill in the chart when you start with B boxes. In this way, they can derive that if they double the number of boxes and look for two consecutive integer factors that multiply to equal 2B, the smaller integer will be the number of boxes that should go on the bottom row. Be sure to have the students explain what to do if no such factors can be found. Some students will suggest using the quadratic formula and if x is not equal to an integer (i.e., x=14.25) then use the integral part of the decimal for the number of boxes on the bottom row and some boxes will be left over.

Emphasize the importance of describing the solution process rather than just focusing on finding a formula. Ask students, "Can you solve this another way?" Since these students are going to teach elementary school, their students will not understand an algebraic solution. Thus, it is important that they try to solve in non-algebraic ways also.

ACTIVITY SOLUTIONS
<u>Problem 1</u>: Part A: 9   Part B: 19, B= x(x+1)/2

<u>Problem 2</u>: 7 tiles

<u>Problem 3</u>: Expect answers such as the following: Problem 2 is two of problem 1 minus one row; they both involve triangles.

Notes 1.4—The Mathematics in the Pages of a Newspaper

MATH CONTENT

- Arithmetic Patterns

MATERIALS

- Sheets of paper that students can use to model a newspaper

CONNECTIONS

- This activity connects with Activity 1.3 in that both deal with summing consecutive whole numbers.

TIMETABLE

- 15 minutes for activity
- 10 minutes for class discussion

ACTIVITY DISCUSSION

Students may want to use two blank sheets to model newspaper pages. In the class discussion following the activity, ask students to make connections between this activity and the cereal box problem (both deal with summing consecutive whole numbers). It will also be useful to ask students to think back on what problem-solving strategies they used in this activity that they have used before (e.g., looking for a pattern).

ACTIVITY SOLUTIONS

1. 4; 8 [For n sheets, 4n pages are formed.]
2. side 1: 1 and 4 one side; side 2: 2 and 3
   [For n sheets, the sum of page numbers on one side of a sheet is $4n + 1$]
   1st sheet, side 1: 1 and 8
   1st sheet, side 2: 2 and 7
   2nd sheet, side 1: 3 and 6
   2nd sheet, side 2: 4 and 5
3. For a single sheet, the sum is 5. For a double sheet, the sum is 9.
4. 10 for a single sheet, 18 for the double
5. 40 pages
   On the innermost sheet, the numbers would be 19 and 22 on one side, 20 and 21 on the other. The sum of these numbers is 82.
   On any one side, the sum is 41.
   The total sum would be $20 \cdot 41 = 820$.
   [For n sheets, the sum of all page numbers in a book is $4n \cdot (4n + 1) \div 2$.]
6. 400 pages
   On the innermost sheet, the numbers would be 199 and 202 on one side, 200 and 201 on the other. The sum of these numbers is 802.
   On any one side, the sum is 401.
   The total sum would be $200 \cdot 401 = 80200$.
7. You would need 7 pages.
   The sum would be 29.
   19 would appear on the same side of the sheet as 8.
8. You would need 12 full and one half sheet to get 50 pages.
   The sum on any one side will be 51.
   43 would appear on the same side of the sheet as 8.

9. There are 5 full and one half page in the section.
   The opposite page would be 67.

Notes 1.5—Family Relations

MATH CONTENT

- Mathematical relations

TIMETABLE

- 20 minutes for activity
- 10 minutes for class discussion

ACTIVITY DISCUSSION

The purpose of this activity is to engage the students in problem solving and to give them the opportunity to use and develop their logical thinking skills. An important point that will arise in doing the activity is the necessity of precision of language. While the students are working on the activity, walk around and observe the students' problem-solving processes. If they are struggling to understand the problems, ask questions like "Using the information about _____, how are A and B related?" Make sure that students are unambiguous in their answers; brother-in-law is ambiguous, but wife's brother is not.

ACTIVITY SOLUTIONS

1. Pat is Frank's mother.
2. Steven is Stephanie's husband's father.
3. Julie is Pat's son's daughter.
4. Mary is Stephanie's husband's sister.
5. Tom is Steven's daughter's husband.
6. Frank is Tom's wife's brother.
7. Tom is Stephanie's husband's sisters' husband.
8. Robert is Tom's son.
9. Julie is Mary's brother's daughter.
10. Robert is Frank's sister's son.
11. Steven
12. Julie
13. Robert
14. Stephanie

Notes 1.6—Constructing Numbers

MATH CONTENT

- Number ideas

CONNECTIONS

- Exercises and More Problems: #34-34, 38

TIMETABLE

- 20 minutes for activity
- 10 minutes for group challenges and class discussion of strategies

ACTIVITY DISCUSSION

This activity involves students in thinking about some basic number ideas and being systematic in constructing numbers that are meet the criteria. These problems can be thought of as optimization problems in some respects. Ask students to describe the strategies that they used in constructing the numbers.

ACTIVITY SOLUTIONS

1. 8,765,493	2. not possible	3. 201,346	4. 98,765,432
5. 102,345,679	6. 501,234,678	7. not possible	8. 498,765
9. 9,876,543,210	10. 1,056,789	11. 943,210	12. not possible
13. 987,651	14. 7523	15. 248,888,888.	

Notes 1.7—The Valentine's Day Party

MATH CONTENT

- Mathematical patterns

MATERIALS

- Person to model problem-solving process (optional)

CONNECTIONS

- Exercises and More Problems: #39
- Either Activity 1.7 or Activity 1.8 could be used with a person modeling the problem-solving process. Both can also be used as problem-solving activities for students.

TIMETABLE

Case #1: Person Models Problem-solving Process
- 10 minutes for students to work on simpler version of problem
- 30-40 minutes for person to solve problem in front of class
- 10 minutes for class discussion of problem-solving process

Case #2: Students Solve Problem
- 30-40 minutes for activity
- 15 minutes for class discussion

ACTIVITY DISCUSSION

It can be helpful for novice problem solvers to watch a more "expert" problem solver in order to observe the process that the expert uses in attempting to solve a novel problem, and see that not all problems are solved in 5 minutes, and that sometimes you try strategies that are dead ends and so you assess your situation and take another tack. One option for this activity is to ask an experienced problem solver to come to the class and solve a problem he or she has not seen before. If you choose to do this, we suggest that you have your students work on the simpler version of "The Valentine's Day Party" (see below) for approximately 10 minutes to get a feel for the problem. Then have the experienced problem solver come to the class, hand him or her the problem, and have him or her solve the problem on the board. After the problem solver has finished, ask him or her to stay for the class discussion about the problem solving.

It is important to choose someone as the modeler who is a good problem solver, does not get easily frustrated, will be reflective about what he or she is doing, and talk aloud about his or her actions during the problem solving process. Talk with the person ahead of time and explain that the goal here is for the students to see (a) an experienced person solve a novel, non-routine problem, (b) that not all problems are solved in 5 minutes, and (c) the type of metacognitive (reflective) thinking that experienced problem solvers use when solving problems.

During the modeling of the problem solving, the students can use the problem-solving observation guide (see below) to make notes of their observations. [You may make copies of this page for your students.] In the discussion following the modeling, discuss the various items on the observation guide and ask the students for their comments in general. It is important to talk about what the problem solver might have been thinking at different stages of the problem. Some points to bring out include that (a) understanding comes in stages (sometimes you have to experience a problem first before fully understanding it), (b) it often takes time to solve a problem, (c) it is important to be systematic, and (d) there are different ways to represent a problem.

If you do not have a problem solver modeling how to solve this problem, you can have the students solve the problem (either the simpler version or the one in Activity 1.7) and have them discuss the strategies they used.

ACTIVITY SOLUTIONS
<u>Simpler version</u>: Joyce Martin shook 2 hands.
<u>Activity 1.7</u>: Joyce Martin shook 4 hands.

<u>Simpler Version of the Problem</u>

The Valentine's Day Party

Three married couples met at a local restaurant for a Valentine's Day dinner party. As each couple arrived, individuals meeting for the first time would shake hands. Each person met a different number of people (0 - 4) for the first time, except for Tom and Joyce Martin, who each met the same number of people. How many hands did Joyce Martin shake?

PROBLEM-SOLVING OBSERVATION GUIDE

PROBLEM:

Understanding the Problem: *What did the problem solver do to try to understand the problem? What assumptions did he or she make about the problem?*

Devising a Plan of Attack: *What strategies did the problem solver think about in developing a plan? How did he or she organize the information? Did the problem solver think about trying a simpler or related problem?*

Carrying Out the Plan: *How did the problem solver implement his or her plan? Did he or she draw a diagram? How did he or she use the diagram? Did the problem solver think his or her plan was appropriate?*

Evaluating the Solution and Thinking About What Has Been Learned: *How did the problem solver go about evaluating his or her solution and solution process? Did he or she try to solve the problem another way? Did the problem solver convince him or herself that the solution process and answer were correct?*

Notes 1.8—The Puzzle of the Hefty Hippos

MATH CONTENT

- Number theory ideas

MATERIALS

- Person to model problem-solving process (optional)

CONNECTIONS

- Exercises and More Problems: #39
- Either Activity 1.7 or Activity 1.8 could be used with a person modeling the problem-solving process. Both can also be used as problem-solving activities for students.

TIMETABLE

Case #1: Person Models Problem-solving Process
- 10 minutes for students to work on simpler version of problem
- 30-40 minutes for person to solve problem in front of class
- 10 minutes for class discussion of problem-solving process

Case #2: Students Solve Problem
- 30-40 minutes for activity
- 15 minutes for class discussion

ACTIVITY DISCUSSION

See Notes 1.7 for a discussion on how this problem could be used with an experienced problem solver modeling the problem-solving process.

If you do not have a problem solver modeling how to solve this problem, you can have the students solve the problem (either the simpler version or the one in Activity 1.8) and have them discuss the strategies they used.

ACTIVITY SOLUTIONS

Simpler version: 178, 185, 200, 210
Activity 1.8: 174, 187, 190, 202, 206, 224

<u>Simpler Version of the Problem</u>

The Puzzle of the Hefty Hippos

Every year the members of the Hefty Hippos Weight Watchers' Club host a volleyball tournament against another group of serious dieters. The tournament has been held on July 4 for the past six years, this year being no exception. The tournament has been such a success that the HHWWWC was able to purchase uniforms for all players last year. When they tried on their uniforms four weeks before this year's tournament, they decided that they had better lose a little weight. They started to meet once a week at the local gym to work off the extra weight they had gained since last year. As an incentive to lose weight, the group decided that the hippo who lost the least amount of weight by the day of the tournament would have to pay for beer and pizza for everyone. On the morning of the tournament the hippos went down to the nearby warehouse to use the heavy duty scales. But the scales started at 300 kg, more than any of them weighed (these were no ordinary hippos). What were they to do? Heloise, a hippo of some considerable mathematical prowess, came up with a solution. She said that they merely needed to weigh all possible pairs of hippos and then determine each hippo's weight from these weights. The weights of all possible pairs were as follows (in kilograms, of course): 363, 378, 385, 388, 395, and 410. How much did each hippo weigh? (You may assume that all weights are whole numbers.)

Notes 1.9—Making Dice

MATH CONTENT

- 3-dimensional geometry, spatial visualization

MATERIALS

- Paper, if needed, to make nets for dice

CONNECTIONS

- Exercises and More Problems: #36

TIMETABLE

- 15 minutes for activity
- 10 minutes for class discussion

ACTIVITY DISCUSSION

This activity engages students in visualizing 3-dimensional objects and using strategies to determine missing numbers.

ACTIVITY SOLUTIONS

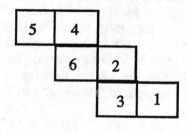

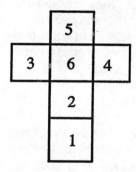

Notes 1.10—The Tower of Hanoi

MATH CONTENT

- Non-linear relationships between two variables

MATERIALS

- Cuisenaire rods (5 rods of different sizes per group)

CONNECTIONS

- Exercises and More Problems: #31-33, 40

TIMETABLE

- 20-30 minutes for activity
- 10 minutes for class discussion

ACTIVITY DISCUSSION

Introduce the Tower of Hanoi activity by telling the students the following legend:

> In the great temple at Benares there is a large brass slab, on which there are three diamond needles each a cubit high and as thick as the body of a bee. At the beginning of the world, God placed 64 gold disks with holes in their centers on one of these needles, the largest resting on the brass slab and the others decreasing in size to the top. This is the Tower of Hanoi. Day and night, priests transfer the disks from needle to needle without deviating from the immutable laws of Hanoi. The priests may move only one disk at a time, and they must place this disk only on a free needle or on top of a larger disk. When the 64 disks have been transferred from the original needle to one of the other needles, the temple will crumble and the world will end. If the priests transfer one disk each second, what is the lifetime of the world? (Adapted from Gudder, S. (1976). *A mathematical journey.* New York: McGraw-Hill.)

Have the students read the conditions of the game in Activity 1.10 and get familiar with the conditions by manipulating the disks (Cuisenaire rods). Observe if the students understand the given conditions. Depending upon the situation, you may have a class discussion to clarify the conditions of the game, or you may only need to discuss the conditions with individual groups.

After the group start working on the activity, observe if some groups decide to solve a simpler problem first (i.e., use fewer disks). If no group decides to do this, you may decide to have the class discuss strategies or plans to facilitate working on the problem. If this is a situation only within a few groups, have these groups discuss their strategies within their groups.

After the groups have had a chance to explore the problem for simpler cases, or even for the given one, they should begin filling in the table. Here the students are to make a conjecture concerning the fewest possible number of moves associated with any number of disks. Walk around the classroom and observe if the students are playing and registering their results on the given table. Observe if they relate the number of disks to the fewest number of moves. If the majority of the groups do not find a pattern, have the whole class discuss strategies for finding a pattern. If only a few groups are having difficulty, have them discuss within their groups.

It should be clear to the students that working in an organized manner with simpler cases is a promising strategy. Comment on the utility of pattern finding with respect to making conjectures or generalizing. Have the students justify that their solution yields the fewest number of moves.

Ask the students to tell what problem-solving strategies they used, or could have used, in this activity. Try to use this problem to being together a number of things learned in this first chapter [organizing information, making conjectures, looking for patterns, trying simpler cases, understanding the problem, making a plan, implementing the plan, evaluating the solution].

ACTIVITY SOLUTIONS
Almost every group will come up with a pattern like this:

# of disks	fewest # of moves
1	1
2	3
3	7
4	15
5	31

Guide them, by asking questions, to generalize this pattern [for n disks, it will take $2^n - 1$ moves for the fewest number of moves]. After the students have completed #31-33 in Exercises and More Problems, ask them to generalize their answers to these questions [if there are an even number of disks, the first move should be to a peg that is not the target peg; if there are an odd number of disks, the first move should be to the target peg]. It is important to emphasize that this generalization was found by looking for the pattern. The students have not proven that the generalization is true. [The generalization involves a recursive procedure and could be proven by induction.]

As an extension, have the students figure out the question posed in the legend of the Tower of Hanoi (i.e., If the priests transfer one disk each second, what is the lifetime of the world?). [Answer: $2^{64} - 1$, which is approximately $5.865 \cdot 10^{11}$ years]

Chapter 2: Numeration

Chapter Overview:

Among the most important topics in elementary school mathematics are those concerned with systems of recording and naming numbers: numeration systems. In this chapter you will learn about the properties of a good numeration system by comparing and contrasting properties of several systems that have been used by various cultures throughout history. Also, in order to help you appreciate the issues involved when young children first begin to learn properties of our base ten (decimal) numeration system, your group will develop one of your own. Finally, you will investigate two special properties of numeration systems—place value and base—in order to help you better understand the roles these properties play in the base ten system we use.

Big Mathematical Ideas:

generalizing, problem-solving strategies, decomposing, mathematical structure, representing

NCTM Standards Links:

K - 4: Mathematics as problem solving; Mathematics as communication; Mathematics as reasoning; Mathematical connections; Number sense & numeration

5 - 8: Mathematics as problem solving; Mathematics as communication; Mathematics as reasoning; Mathematical connections; Number & number relationship; Number systems & number theory

Chapter Outline:

Notes 2.1—Early Numeration Systems

MATH CONTENT

- Numeration systems

MATERIALS

- *Resource Manual*

CONNECTIONS

- Exercises and More Problems: #45-46
- Students will need to read the Historical/Social/Cultural Notes about Numeration in Chapter 2 of the *Resource Manual* before completing this activity. The reading could be done before coming to class.

TIMETABLE

- 10 minutes for activity
- 5 minutes for class discussion

ACTIVITY DISCUSSION

This activity could be assigned to students to do outside of class before working on Activity 2.2 in class. This activity engages students in examining and working with a number of different numeration systems. During the discussion, have the students discuss what is a numeration system.

ACTIVITY SOLUTIONS

1.   13 would be represented by 13 tally marks; 24 by 24 tally marks; 56 by 56 tally marks; 104 by 104 tally marks

2.   345

1,039

12,678

Notes 2.2—The Hindu-Arabic Numeration System

MATH CONTENT

- Characteristics and properties of numeration systems

CONNECTIONS

- Exercises and More Problems: #3, 36

TIMETABLE

- 20 minutes for activity
- 10 minutes for class discussion

ACTIVITY DISCUSSION

This activity has students explore characteristics and properties of the Hindu-Arabic numeration system. In this activity, students are generalizing the rules of use [mathematical structure].

ACTIVITY SOLUTIONS

1. base 10; the Hindu-Arabic numeration systems has groups of 10 and all numbers are written in terms of powers of 10; for example, in the numeral 231 the 1 represents 1 group of 10^0, 3 represents 3 groups of 10^1, and 2 represents 2 groups of 10^2
2. in the numeral 232, the far right 2 represents 2 but the far left 2 represents 200
3. in the numeral 564, the 4 represents $4 \cdot 10$, the six represents $6 \cdot 10$, and the 5 represents $5 \cdot 100$
4. in the numeral 1847, the individual symbols represent 7, 40, 800 and 1,000 and the set of symbols, 1847 represents $7 + 40 + 800 + 1000$
5. the zero in 906 represents 0 groups of 10 or $0 \cdot 10$; if it was not there, nine hundred six would be indistinguishable from ninety-six when written in symbols
6. if some numerals did not represent unique numbers then you would not know which number was being referred to (see #5 above)
7. A *number* is an idea that represents a quantity. A *numeral* is the symbol we use to represent a number. For example, the symbol "5" represents the quantity of five. A *name* of a number is the word that we use to call the number or numeral. Different languages use different names to represent the same quantity or idea.

Notes 2.3—Comparing Numeration Systems

MATH CONTENT

- Characteristics and properties of numeration systems

CONNECTIONS

- Exercises and More Problems: #48

TIMETABLE

- 15 minutes for activity
- 5-10 minutes for class discussion

ACTIVITY DISCUSSION

This activity has students compare characteristics and properties of different numeration systems. In this activity, students are generalizing the rules of use [mathematical structure]. During the class discussion, have different groups justify their characterizations of certain systems.

ACTIVITY SOLUTIONS

1. advantages—easy to remember and write the symbols; disadvantages—have to count tally marks to figure out number, cumbersome for large numbers
2. The Egyptian system is additive because value of a numeral is the sum of the value of each individual symbol.
3. The Egyptian system allows you to express large numbers with a single symbol, and thus large numbers that do not have a single symbol can still be expressed fairly concisely. Also, you do not have to count many symbols like tally marks.
4. The Babylonian system used the idea of place value in that the spaces separated one place from another, and the same symbol placed in different places would have different values.
5. The absence of a zero can cause confusion because it is hard to tell how many spaces there are between symbols and if there are any spaces to the right of a numeral.
6. The Chinese-Japanese numeration system is a base ten system because numerals are grouped by tens and written in terms of powers of ten.
7. advantage—has a base; disadvantages—symbols are difficult to remember and write, no symbol for zero
8. A subtractive property was introduced in this system in order to avoid writing a symbol more than three times. This was done by placing symbols representing smaller numbers to the left of symbols representing larger ones, as, in writing 4 as IV, instead of IIII, or 900 as CM, instead of DIIII. A limited multiplicative property is also evident in the Roman numeration system. A bar placed over a symbol indicates that the value of the symbol must be multiplied by 1000. Thus

   $\overline{V}$ represents 5000, and $\overline{CDX}$ represents 410 • 1000.

   More than one bar can be placed over symbols to indicate multiplication by greater powers of 1000. Thus,

   $\overline{\overline{LX}}$ represents 60 • 1000 • 1000.
9. no, because in the numeral VIII, each I stands for 1

Notes 2.4—Mathematical and Non-mathematical
Characteristics of Systems

MATH CONTENT

- Characteristics and properties of numeration systems

TIMETABLE

- 10 minutes for activity
- 10 minutes for class discussion

ACTIVITY DISCUSSION

This activity has students generalizing the rules of use [mathematical structure]. During the class discussion, have different groups justify their characterizations of certain systems.

ACTIVITY SOLUTIONS

1. Number of digits used are 1, 7, 2, 12, 7, 10
2. Note: Some of these answers are open to debate and can provide a good discussion.

Primitive—additive; unique representation; convenient, easy to use; ease with which it can be learned

Egyptian—additive; has base; unique representation; convenient, easy to use; ease with it can be learned

Babylonian—additive; multiplicative; has base; place value

Chinese-Japanese—additive; multiplicative; has base; unique representation

Roman—additive; unique representation; economical in terms of number of distinct symbols; ease with which it can be learned

Hindu-Arabic—additive; multiplicative; has base; place value; symbol for zero; unique representation; convenient, easy to use; economical in terms of number of distinct symbols; ease with which it can be learned

Notes 2.5—Creating a Numeration System

MATH CONTENT

- Characteristics and properties of numeration systems

CONNECTIONS

- This activity is a good culminating activity for the students' work on numeration systems.

TIMETABLE

- 15 minutes for activity
- 15 minutes for sharing of numeration systems

ACTIVITY DISCUSSION

This activity has students draw on what they know about numeration systems and create their own. The sharing of their own numeration systems is a time for the groups to practice explaining clearly and concisely a mathematical system. One suggestion is for groups to exchange their systems and figure out what characteristics are present in each system. It may be useful to provide groups with a constraint, such as using three or four of the characteristics in making up their own system. An interesting discussion may arise concerning whether having some characteristics implies having others. This discussion is important for helping students to learn to communicate mathematically.

ACTIVITY SOLUTIONS
answers will vary

Notes 2.6—Exploring Place Value Through Trading Games

MATH CONTENT

- Concepts of grouping, trading and place value, different bases

MATERIALS

- Base four blocks (1 cube, 14 flats, 14 longs, 14 units per group), two spinners per group

CONNECTIONS

- Exercises and More Problems: #35, 39-40, 49

TIMETABLE

- 30 minutes for activity
- 15 minutes for class discussion

ACTIVITY DISCUSSION

It is important to provide a rationale to the students for why we are doing activities involving different numeration systems, different bases, etc. Two fundamental reasons are that working with ideas of numeration will (1) help them better understand the Hindu-Arabic numeration system, and (2) put them in the same situation as a child who is learning a numeration system for the first time. It is also important to correctly use the language involved with different bases. For example, 12base three is read as "one two base three", not "twelve base three". Obviously, twelve has no meaning in a base three system.

For the playing of the games have group members pair up and play pair against pair. The purpose of the "310 (Fifty-Two)" game is to have the students involved in adding with regrouping. The purpose of the "Give Away" game is to involve the students in subtracting and trading in. Take note of the way in which the students keep record of their totals. At any time, the students should be able to tell you the number of units they have, as well as the number of flats, longs and units. Note: If you do not have base four blocks, you can copy the pages following the solutions (one for each group) and have the students cut them out before coming to class.

During the discussion following the two grouping and trading games, have the discussion focus on the meaning of the terms grouping, trading and place value and how they are different from one another. The idea of decomposition is present here in the breaking down of flats into longs and longs into units in the process of grouping and trading. The big idea of multiple representations should be emphasized as numbers can be represented in different ways by using different bases, using numerals and base blocks, etc.

ACTIVITY SOLUTIONS
310 (Fifty-Two)
1. 2 spins; any combination of two spins adding up to at least 16
2. infinite number of spins; can keep adding or subtracting as needed to have less than a flat
3. 12 units
4. grouping, trading, place value

Give Away
1. 3 spins; any combination of spins adding up to exactly 32
2. infinite number of spins; can keep adding or subtracting as needed to have some blocks

3. 9 spins; any combination of spins adding up to exactly 98
4. same as #2
5. grouping, trading, place value

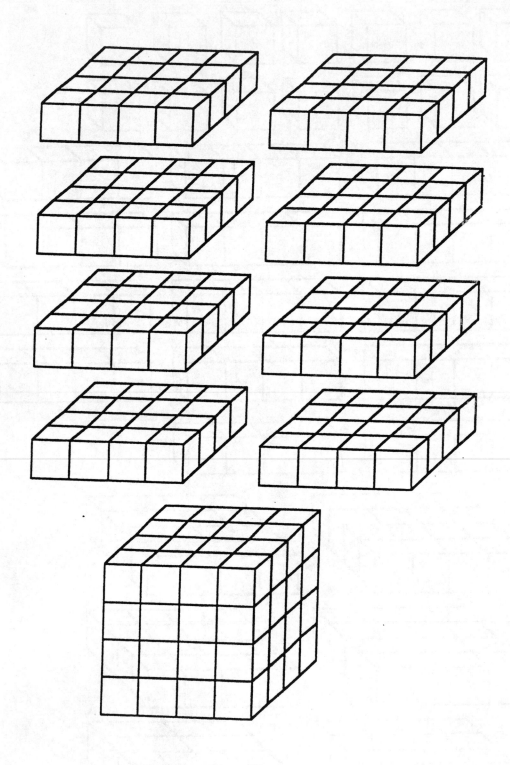

Notes 2.7—Converting from One Base to Another

MATH CONTENT

- Concepts of grouping, trading and place value, different bases, changing from one base to another

MATERIALS

- Base four blocks (as needed)

CONNECTIONS

- Exercises and More Problems: #38, 50

TIMETABLE

- 30 minutes for activity
- 5-10 minutes for class discussion

ACTIVITY DISCUSSION

The discussion of this activity should involve students in sharing their strategies for changing from one base to another. Have the students make a generalization about this process. Have students give their justifications for picking the largest number and discuss whether it is necessary to change all the numerals to base ten first or whether it is possible by looking at the numerals in the highest place only.

ACTIVITY SOLUTIONS

1. 110_{two}, 11_{five}, 10_{six}
    11010_{two}, 41_{five}, 33_{six}
    101101_{two}, 140_{five}, 113_{six}
    100111_{two}, 124_{five}, 103_{six}
2. 3, 23, 29, 16
3. 101_{three}, 76_{eight}, ET_{twelve}, 325_{twelve}

Notes 2.8—Place Value and Different Bases

MATH CONTENT

- Place value, different bases, changing from one base to another

CONNECTIONS

- Exercises and More Problems: #51

TIMETABLE

- 15 minutes for activity
- 5-10 minutes for class discussion

ACTIVITY DISCUSSION

This activity gives students a chance to pull together ideas of place value and base, and compare a base ten system with a base two system. Have students verbalize their procedures for changing from one base to another. This will help them develop the abililty to communicate mathematically.

ACTIVITY SOLUTIONS

1. it means that numbers are grouped by tens, all numbers are written in terms of powers of ten, and the value of each digit is determined by its position in the numeral
2. the difference is that numbers are grouped by twos and all numbers are written in terms of powers of two
3. To convert a number from base ten to a given base, say n, divide the number by n. This will give you a quotient and a remainder. The remainder is the far right digit in the required number written in base n. Now, divide the numerator from the previous step by n again. This will again give you a quotient and a remainder. The remainder is the second digit from the right in the required number. Divide the numerator by n again. Repeat this process until the quotient you get is smaller than the base. Then the final quotient will be the far left digit in the required number, and the remainders, written in the reverse order in which you got them give you the rest of the number.
4. We start by writing the given numeral in expanded notation. It is then easy to calculate the value of the number in base ten.

Notes 2.9—Solving a Problem with a Different Base

MATH CONTENT

- Different bases

CONNECTIONS

- Exercises and More Problems: #44, 47

TIMETABLE

- 30 minutes for activity
- 10 minutes for class discussion

ACTIVITY DISCUSSION

This problem engages students in solving a problem that can be represented in another base (base two).

ACTIVITY SOLUTIONS

By making an organized list students may gain insight into the solution of the problem. Solving a simpler problem may allow the students to discover that the key to the problem is that either a bag is light (from a car with 90 lb. bags) or it is not (from a car with 100 lb. bags). So the situation can be modeled by writing the numbers in base two. For example, if there are 43 light bags, then $43 = 101011_{two}$ and thus the light bags come from cars 1, 2, 4 and 6. The students should try to form a generalization about this problem.

Notes 2.10—Computations in Different Bases

MATH CONTENT

- Performing computations in different bases

CONNECTIONS

- Exercises and More Problems: #52

TIMETABLE

- 30 minutes for activity
- 10 minutes for class discussion

ACTIVITY DISCUSSION

Students may need to be reminded that doing operations in other bases helps them understand our base ten system better and puts them in the position of children learning to do operations in the base ten system. When the students are doing computations in different bases be sure that they are viewing 12three as "one two base three" rather than "twelve base three." Also, when regrouping numerals make sure the students are writing the regrouped numeral in the given base and not in base ten.

ACTIVITY SOLUTIONS

1. 1211four, E90twelve, 1two, 62seven, 2010four, 2404six, 20715nine
2. two different illustrations are possible: draw base ten blocks, circle groups of two, and then count the number of groups of two; draw base ten blocks, separate equally into two groups, and then figure out the number in one group
3. use methods similar to those described in #2
4. eleven, two, twelve
5. 3421, 4532, 2321, 1214

Chapter 3: Operations with Natural Numbers, Whole Numbers & Integers

Chapter Overview:

A solid understanding of addition, subtraction, multiplication, and division is crucial to being able to do mathematics and these operations play central parts in the elementary school mathematics curriculum. In this chapter you will study the various models (representations) for these operations involving natural numbers, whole numbers, and integers and explore different computational techniques (called algorithms). Special attention will be placed on developing deep understanding of each of the four operations and the wide range of algorithms that have been developed for doing large number computations.

Big Mathematical Ideas:

mathematical structure, verifying, generalizing, using algorithms

NCTM Standards Links:

K - 4: Mathematics as problem solving; Mathematics as communication; Mathematics as reasoning; Mathematical connections; Concepts of whole number operations; Whole number computation

5 - 8: Mathematics as problem solving; Mathematics as communication; Mathematics as reasoning; Mathematical connections; Computation & estimation

Chapter Outline:

Notes 3.1—Exploring Sets of Numbers

MATH CONTENT

- Properties and characteristics of sets of numbers

CONNECTIONS

- Exercises and More Problems: #37-38
- Students will need to read the Explanations Concerning Operations in Chapter 3 of the *Resource Manual* before completing this activity. The reading could be done before coming to class.

TIMETABLE

- 30 minutes for activity
- 10-15 minutes for class discussion

ACTIVITY DISCUSSION

This activity could be assigned to students to do outside of class before working on Activity 3.2 in class. This activity engages students in examining and working with a different sets of numbers. The discussion can help in bringing to the surface questions and misconceptions about the field properties and the different sets of numbers.

ACTIVITY SOLUTIONS

1. m, r, n, o, k, l, t, s, q, p
2. the set of Whole numbers includes 0
3. the set of Natural numbers is a subset of the set of Whole numbers
4. these sets are both subsets of the set of Integers
5.

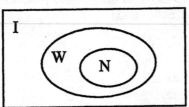

6. it means that if you add any two integers, the sum will be an integer; it means that if you multiply any two integers, the product will be an integer
7. no, when dividing one integer by another integer it is possible to get a number that is not an integer, such as $3 \div 4 = 3/4$
8. yes, if you subtract any two integers, the difference will be an integer; this is true since the set of Integers includes negative and positive numbers
9. yes, if you add any two whole numbers you will get a whole number; yes, if you multiply any two whole numbers you will get a whole number; no, if you subtract one whole number from another whole number it is possible to get a negative number which cannot be in the set of Whole numbers; no, if you divide one whole number by another whole number it is possible to get a number that is not a whole number
10. same as for whole numbers
11. the set that contains other sets is closed under the same operations as the subsets and has the possibility of being closed under additional operations
12. $4 + 6 = 6 + 4$ demonstrates the commutative property for addition on the set of Natural numbers, Whole numbers or Integers; $4 - 7 \neq 7 - 4$ demonstrates that the commutative

property for subtraction does not hold on the set of Integers, Whole numbers or Natural numbers

13. answers will vary; one possibility is the switch around property

14. $(3 \cdot (-4)) \cdot 2 = -12 \cdot 2 = -24$; $3 \cdot (-4 \cdot 2) = 3 \cdot (-8) = -24$; this demonstrates the associative property for multiplication on the set of Integers; $(8 \div 4) \div 2 = 4 \div 2 = 2$; $8 \div (4 \div 2) = 8 \div 2 = 4$; this demonstrates that the associative property for division does not hold on the set of Integers, Whole numbers or Natural numbers

15. answers will vary; one possibility is the grouping property

16. yes, 0 is the identity element for addition for the set of Integers, Whole numbers and Natural numbers

17. yes, 1 is the identity element for multiplication for the set of Integers, Whole numbers and Natural numbers

18. the set of Integers has an additive inverse for every element of the set

19. none of these sets has a multiplicative inverse for every element of the set

20. We say a given set has an identity under a given operation if the set has a unique element, say I, so that when you perform the operation with this element and any other element, say x, in the set, the result of the operation is x. Algebraically, we say that the set has an identity I, under the operation *, if, for any element x in the set, we find, $I * x = x * I = x$. It is important to note that the element I should be unique. If such an element exists, we say that I is the * identity for that set.

21. We say that an element, say x, belonging to this set has an inverse, if, for that element, we can find another element, say y, in the same set so that, when we perform the operation on x and y, the result is the identity of the set for that operation. Algebraically, we say, that an element x has an inverse under the operation * in a given set with * identity I, if we can find an element y in the same set so that $x * y = y * x = I$. If such an element exists, we say that y is the * inverse of x, and vice versa.

22. the commutative properties for addition and multiplication for the set of Integers allow us to solve algebraic equations

23. if the set of Integers was not closed under addition, subtraction, and multiplication then it would be difficult to do algebraic manipulations; because the set of Integers is not closed under division, this raises the need for a larger set that includes numbers that are formed by the division of two integers—the set of Rational numbers

Notes 3.2—Sets and Their Properties

MATH CONTENT

- Properties and characteristics of sets

TIMETABLE

- 15 minutes for activity
- 10 minutes for class discussion

ACTIVITY DISCUSSION

During the class discussion, have the students verify their answers concerning the properties that are valid for each set and its operation. On #3, there is no need to confuse students by discussing composition of permutations, but they can use the diagram, the individual rotations and flips, and the chart to visualize the operation of composition. Encourage the students to use a triangle to actually see the result of applying the operation to two elements of the set. Emphasize the connection here between geometric transformations and properties of numbers.

Wrap up the discussion by discussing the mathematical structure involved in each of the sets, emphasizing that it is this structure that allows us to solve problems in those sets (e.g., set of integers). Emphasize that mathematical structure is fundamental to doing mathematics; a big part of the job of mathematicians is to look for underlying structure.

ACTIVITY SOLUTIONS

1. a. yes, it is closed under & since operating on any two elements under & yields an element of the set
   b. yes, it is commutative and associative for &; all cases can be tested to verify this
   c. square is the & identity
   d. yes, each element has an inverse

2. a. no, the set is not closed under * since $1 * 5 = 2 (1) - 5 = -3$ which is not in the set of Whole numbers
   b. no, it is not commutative or associative; $1 * 5 = -3$, $5 * 1 = 9$; $(2 * 3) * 4 = -2$, $2 * (3 * 4) = 2$
   c. no, there is not a unique identity because each element operated with itself will yield the element
   d. no, since there is no identity, having an inverse does not make sense

3. the set is closed under the operation; it is not commutative since $R2 * F1 = F2$ but $F1 * R2 = F3$; it is associative; R1 is the identity; every element has an inverse

Notes 3.3—Classifying Word Problems by Operation

MATH CONTENT

- Arithmetic operations

TIMETABLE

- 15 minutes for activity
- 10 minutes for class discussion

ACTIVITY DISCUSSION

Have the students group the story problem situations by operation. Then encourage them to group the problems within the operation into sets of the same type of problem. Ask the students to give their classifications and the names they used for the categories. Discuss the groupings and try to arrive at a consensus. The students will have fairly good names that describe the categories and at the end of the discussion you can present the "standard" name for these categories, as shown below, and discuss why these names are used.

ACTIVITY SOLUTIONS

Addition (one type)

#2 $2 + 3 = ?$ #12 $7 + 20 = ?$

Subtraction (three types)

Comparison	**Take Away**	**Missing Addend**
#1 $8 - 3 = ?$	#7 $8 - 5 = ?$	#5 $2 + ? = 8$
#13 $14 - 9 = ?$	#15 $6 - 2 = ?$	#17 $7 + ? = 14$

Multiplication (three types)

Repeated Addition	**Cross Product**	**Array**
#6 $4 \times 3 = ?$ $(3+3+3+3)$	#3 $3 \times 4 = ?$	#9 $8 \times 7 = ?$
#16 $5 \times 3 = ?$ $(3+3+3+3+3)$	#10 $6 \times 8 = ?$	#14 $16 \times 8 = ?$

Division (two types)

Repeated Subtraction	**Sharing**
#8 $45 \div 5 = ?$ $(45-5-5-5-5-5-5-5-5-5)$	#4 $45 \div 9 = ?$
#18 $66 \div 2 = ?$	#11 $80 \div 10 = ?$

Notes 3.4—Integer Addition and Subtraction

MATH CONTENT

- Addition and subtraction with signed numbers

TIMETABLE

- 20 minutes for activity
- 5-10 minutes for class discussion

ACTIVITY DISCUSSION

Have students explain their models for adding and subtracting signed numbers. Encourage students to verbalize a general procedure.

ACTIVITY SOLUTIONS

1. answers will vary; some possibilities include temperature, stocks, football yardage; yes, negative numbers are necessary to represent loss
2. a. 3 + (-2) can be modeled by starting at 0, moving 3 units to the right, then moving 2 units to the left; (-3) + 2 can be modeled by starting at 0, moving 3 units to the left, then moving 2 units to the right; (-2) + (-3) can be modeled by starting at 0, moving 2 units to the left, then moving 3 more units to the left
   b. 12 - (-7) can be modeled by starting at 0, moving 12 units to the right, then moving 7 more units to the right; (-5) - 8 can be modeled by starting at 0, moving 5 units to the left, then moving 8 more units to the left; (-6) - (-6) can be modeled by starting at 0, moving 6 units to the left, then moving 6 units to the right
3. a. 0   b. 53°F   c. The team lost 1 yard   d. He gained $45.
4. Harry's debt is bigger by $700.
5. a. 1150 - 250 - 348 - 628 - 25 + 786 - 350 - 440 - 25 + 500
   b. The final balance will be $370.

Notes 3.5—Integer Multiplication and Division

MATH CONTENT

- Multiplication and division with signed numbers

TIMETABLE

- 20 minutes for activity
- 5-10 minutes for class discussion

ACTIVITY DISCUSSION
Have students explain their models for multiplying and dividing signed numbers. Encourage students to verbalize a general procedure.

ACTIVITY SOLUTIONS
1.
$$2 \cdot -5 = -10$$
$$1 \cdot -5 = -5$$
$$0 \cdot -5 = 0$$
$$-1 \cdot -5 = 5$$
$$-2 \cdot -5 = 10$$
$$-3 \cdot -5 = 15$$

2. a.

Minutes Passed	Temperature
0	60°
1	58°
2	56°
3	54°
4	52°
5	50°

   b. The temperature will reach 0° F at 1:30 p. m.
   c. At 2:30 p. m., the temperature will be −120° F.

3. you could construct a pattern where the dividend is the number that is decreasing (or increasing) each time by the amount of the divisor

4.
$$16 \div -4 = -4$$
$$12 \div -4 = -3$$
$$8 \div -4 = -2$$
$$4 \div -4 = -1$$
$$0 \div -4 = 0$$
$$-4 \div -4 = 1$$
$$-8 \div -4 = 2$$
$$-12 \div -4 = 3$$

5. a. The sea level can be regarded as the zero level.
   b. The average depth will be 47 feet below the sea level.

6. He lost $800 on each transaction.

Notes 3.6—Scratch Addition Algorithm

MATH CONTENT

- Addition algorithm

TIMETABLE

- 15 minutes for activity
- 5-10 minutes for class discussion

ACTIVITY DISCUSSION

Demonstrate how to use the algorithm on the board and have the students work along. Your job is only to **demonstrate** the algorithm—**do not** explain the algorithm. Then have them work the additional problem in their groups and discuss why the algorithm works. **Allow the students time to hash this out.** Have the students share and verify their explanations. Relate the concept of an algorithm to the work the students did in describing a general procedure for changing a number from one base to another.

ACTIVITY SOLUTIONS

The scratch addition algorithm allows one to perform complicated additions by adding only two single digits. Each time the sum of two single digits is equal to the base or more, one records this sum by making a "scratch" line through the last digit added and writing the number of units next to the scratched digit. When a column of additions is complete, write the number of units below the addition line. Then count the number of scratch lines and add this number to the next column.

Activity 3.6

1442_{five}, 1052_{seven}

Explanation: The scratch addition algorithm works because each scratch marks represents a group of ten, and the number of scratches in a column is the number of tens carried to the next column. The algorithm is convenient because it only involves adding two single-digit numbers at a time.

Notes 3.7—Lattice Multiplication Algorithm

MATH CONTENT

- Multiplication algorithm

TIMETABLE

- 15 minutes for activity
- 5-10 minutes for class discussion

ACTIVITY DISCUSSION

Demonstrate how to use the algorithm on the board and have the students work along. Your job is only to **demonstrate** the algorithm—**do not** explain the algorithm. Then have them work the additional problem in their groups and discuss why the algorithm works. **Allow the students time to hash this out.** Have the students share and verify their explanations. Relate the concept of an algorithm to the work the students did in describing a general procedure for changing a number from one base to another.

ACTIVITY SOLUTIONS

For the lattice multiplication algorithm, a rectangle is partitioned into a lattice with the number of rectangular regions within the large rectangle depending upon the number of digits in the factors. In the case below, the product being performed is 27 • 53 so a 2 x 2 lattice is formed with each rectangular region cut in half on the diagonal. Starting with the lower right rectangular region, the column number (7) is multiplied by the row number (3). When recording the product, the tens are written above the diagonal and the units are written below. The each column number is multiplied by each row number. When the multiplication is complete, add along the diagonals and regroup to the next diagonal if the sum of the digits exceeds the base.

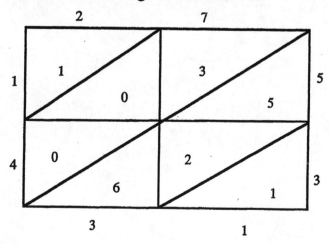

Thus, 27 • 53 = 1431.

Activity 3.7

322; 19,320

Explanation: The spatial arrangement of the factors along the lattice allow for the diagonals of the lattice to serve as the decimal place columns of the product.

Notes 3.8—Cashiers' Algorithm

MATH CONTENT

- Subtraction algorithm

CONNECTIONS

- Exercises and More Problems: #43

TIMETABLE

- 10 minutes for activity
- 5 minutes for class discussion

ACTIVITY DISCUSSION

For this algorithm, the students should be able to read and understand the algorithm without you demonstrating it.

ACTIVITY SOLUTIONS

$27

You will count off and return the money as 62, 63, 64, 65, 70, 80, 100.

Explanation: The cashier's algorithm for subtraction uses the missing addend approach to subtraction, that is, a - b = c if and only if b + c = a. The money is counted off in terms of the bills that the cashier gives you. Thus, as the cashier counts 23, 24, and 25, you get one dollar bill each time; for 25, 30, you get a five dollar bill, and so on.

Notes 3.9—Austrian Subtraction Algorithm

MATH CONTENT

- Subtraction algorithm

CONNECTIONS

- Exercises and More Problems: #44

TIMETABLE

- 10 minutes for activity
- 5 minutes for class discussion

ACTIVITY DISCUSSION

Demonstrate how to use the algorithm on the board and have the students work along. Your job is only to **demonstrate** the algorithm—**do not** explain the algorithm. Then have them work the additional problem in their groups and discuss why the algorithm works. **Allow the students time to hash this out.** Have the students share and verify their explanations. Relate the concept of an algorithm to the work the students did in describing a general procedure for changing a number from one base to another.

ACTIVITY SOLUTIONS

$$
\begin{array}{ccc}
7 & 2 & 1 \\
-\ 3 & 4 & 8 \\
\end{array}
\qquad
\begin{array}{cccc}
7 & 2 & 11 \\
-\ 3 & 5 & 8 \\
\hline
 & & 3 \\
\end{array}
$$

$$
\begin{array}{ccc}
7 & 12 & 11 \\
-\ 4 & 5 & 8 \\
\hline
3 & 7 & 3 \\
\end{array}
$$

Explanation: Adding 10 ones is the same as adding 1 ten; adding 10 tens is the same as adding 1 hundred and by the addition property of equality, if $a - b = x$, then $a = x + b$ and $a + c = x + b + c$ and $(a + c) - (b + c) = x$.

Notes 3.10—Russian Peasant Algorithm

MATH CONTENT

- Multiplication algorithm

CONNECTIONS

- Exercises and More Problems: #39, 45

TIMETABLE

- 20-30 minutes for activity
- 10 minutes for class discussion

ACTIVITY DISCUSSION

Note: This algorithm is rather involved and will take some time for students to grapple with why it works. Demonstrate how to use the algorithm on the board and have the students work along. Your job is only to **demonstrate** the algorithm—**do not** explain the algorithm. Then have them work the additional problem in their groups and discuss why the algorithm works. **Allow the students time to hash this out.** Have the students share and verify their explanations. Relate the concept of an algorithm to the work the students did in describing a general procedure for changing a number from one base to another.

In the final discussion wrapping up work on algorithms, bring out the idea of generalizing procedures into algorithms and the way in which each operation can have multiple representations (many algorithms for the same operation).

ACTIVITY SOLUTIONS

Shown below is the algorithm for finding $74 \cdot 18$.

Halving		Doubling
~~74~~	•	~~18~~
37	•	36
~~18~~	•	~~72~~
9	•	144
~~4~~	•	~~288~~
~~2~~	•	~~576~~
1	•	1152

So, $74 \cdot 18 = 36 + 144 + 1152 = 1332$.

Explanation: Write the first factor in base two representation and multiply the base ten value of each digit in the representation by the second factor. Then sum these products for the answer. For $27 \cdot 51$, if 27 is written in base two it would be 11011_{two} or $(1 \cdot 16) + (1 \cdot 8) + (0 \cdot 4) + (1 \cdot 2) + (1 \cdot 1)$. Note that $16 \cdot 51 = 816$; $8 \cdot 51 = 408$; $2 \cdot 51 = 102$; $1 \cdot 51 = 51$ and $16 + 8 + 2 + 1 = 27$. The students may need a hint to start them thinking about why this algorithm works.

Notes 3.11—Using Algorithms to Solve Problems

MATH CONTENT

- Algorithms

CONNECTIONS

- Exercises and More Problems: #40-42, 47

TIMETABLE

- 20 minutes for activity
- 10 minutes for class discussion

ACTIVITY DISCUSSION

Working backwards and guess and check are two strategies that may be useful in working these problems. During the discussion of this activity have the students give their solutions and explain their strategies in solving the problems.

Tie in ideas of different operation types with the missing digits problems. For example, #1 involves missing addend subtraction problems. If students are having difficulty finding missing digits (e.g., #4), suggest that they find a method of keeping their thinking recorded.

ACTIVITY SOLUTIONS

1. 303, 254, 1001
   answers will vary
   145, 322, 511
2. 562, 3942, 8817, 13321
3. answers will vary
4. M=1, O=0, S=9; these are the only values because M must be 1 which forces the other digits

Notes 3.12—Operation Applications

MATH CONTENT

- Algorithms

CONNECTIONS

- Exercises and More Problems: #46

TIMETABLE

- 20 minutes for activity
- 10 minutes for class discussion

ACTIVITY DISCUSSION

Guess and check and drawing a picture may be useful in solving these problems. The strategy of using an equation can make the solutions of the problems on page 80 easier to find.

ACTIVITY SOLUTIONS

1. x, -, ÷
   +, ÷, +
   ÷, +, +
   ÷, +, x
   x, +, +
   +, x, -
   +, +, x
   x, -, x
2. 10, 14, 9
3. 42
4. 1568
5. $[5(2x + 5) - 25] \div 10 = x$
6. $(3x + 8 + x) \div 4 - x = 2$
7. $(x + x + 1 + 11) \div 2 - x = 6$
8. answers will vary

Chapter 4: Number Theory

Chapter Overview:

Number theory is a branch of mathematics that involves the study of numbers and, in particular, the natural numbers. In this chapter you will be introduced to prime and composite numbers and investigate the concepts of divisibility, greatest common divisor, and least common multiple—concepts that are fundamental to understanding operations on fractions. An especially interesting aspect of this chapter is that you will see that there are some quite challenging and valuable problems involving what appears at first glance to be a very simple branch of mathematics. A final important feature of this chapter is that you will begin to learn how to construct mathematical proofs.

Big Mathematical Ideas:

> conjecturing, decomposing, verifying, problem-solving strategies, and representing

NCTM Standards Links:

> *K - 4:* Mathematics as problem solving; Mathematics as communication; Mathematics as reasoning; Mathematical connections; Number sense & numeration; Concepts of whole number operations; Patterns & relationships

> *5 - 8:* Mathematics as problem solving; Mathematics as communication; Mathematics as reasoning; Mathematical connections; Number systems & number theory; Patterns & functions

Chapter Outline:

Notes 4.1—The Locker Problem

MATH CONTENT

- Prime numbers, composite numbers, factors, square numbers

CONNECTIONS

- Exercises and More Problems: #78, 79

TIMETABLE

- 20 minutes for activity
- 10-15 minutes for class discussion

ACTIVITY DISCUSSION

The locker problem provides the students with a problem-solving situation from which will emerge fundamental number theory concepts. It is important that the students have time to explore and grasp the essence of the problem and its solution before any introduction to the chapter.

ACTIVITY SOLUTIONS

By making an organized list, students can keep track of which locker doors remain open. Using the list, students can attempt to find the pattern by making and testing conjectures. Solving a simpler problem (e.g., 20 lockers) can be a way to find the pattern without having to deal with all the numbers. Students can then make a generalization for any number of lockers. The pattern is that the locker numbers with an odd number of factors will be left open because these lockers are handled an odd number of times (open - close - open, etc.). These numbers are perfect squares. Ask questions such as, "Why are all numbers with an odd number of factors perfect squares?" to force the students to justify their answers. The lockers that will remain open are lockers 1, 4, 9, 16, 25, 36, 49, 64, 81, and 100.

Notes 4.2—Searching for Patterns of Factors

MATH CONTENT

- Prime numbers, composite numbers, factors, prime factorization

CONNECTIONS

- Exercises and More Problems: #61-62

TIMETABLE

- 15 minutes for activity
- 10 minutes for class discussion

ACTIVITY DISCUSSION

The discussion of this activity should focus not only on the classification of integers by the number of factors, but also how the factorization of integers has multiple representations: as the prime factorization, as represented graphically, or as a factor tree. Many students will notice the patterns of numbers on the graph and a good discussion can be generated by investigating how to prove some of the patterns, and examining the slopes of the lines on the completed graph and why certain lines have certain slopes. The idea of decomposition as it relates to breaking integers into their prime factorization should be discussed, as well as the role of the number 1 as a factor (i.e., Is it important to consider 1 as a factor of every integer?).

ACTIVITY SOLUTIONS

answers will vary on the patterns observed in the graph

Number	List of all factors	# of factors	"prime or prime factorization
2	1, 2	2	prime
3	1, 3	2	prime
4	1, 2, 4	3	2•2
5	1, 5	2	prime
6	1, 2, 3, 6	4	2•3
7	1, 7	2	prime
8	1, 2, 4, 8	4	2•2•2
9	1, 3, 9	3	3•3
10	1, 2, 5, 10	4	2•5
11	1, 11	2	prime
12	1, 2, 3, 4, 6, 12	6	2•2•3
13	1, 13	2	prime
14	1, 2, 7, 14	4	2•7
15	1, 3, 5, 15	4	3•5
16	1, 2, 4, 8, 16	5	2•2•2•2
17	1, 17	2	prime
18	1, 2, 3, 6, 9, 18	6	2•3•3
19	1, 19	2	prime
20	1, 2, 4, 5, 10, 20	6	2•2•5
21	1, 3, 7, 21	4	3•7
22	1, 2, 11, 22	4	2•11
23	1, 23	2	prime

24	1, 2, 3, 4, 5, 8, 12, 24	8	2•2•2•3
25	1, 5, 25	3	5•5

Notes 4.3—Factor Feat: A Game of Factors

MATH CONTENT

- Prime numbers, composite numbers, factors

CONNECTIONS

- Exercises and More Problems: #82

TIMETABLE

- 15 minutes for activity
- 10 minutes for class discussion

ACTIVITY DISCUSSION

Factor Feat can take quite a bit of time if play continues until all numbers are marked. Setting a time limit (e.g., 10 minutes) might be helpful. After time has been called, have the students discuss what strategies they used in selecting numbers, both early and late in the game. Discuss how their strategies might change if the winner is the player with the largest number of marks instead of the sum of marked numbers.

Notes 4.4—Classifying Numbers According to Prime Factorization

MATH CONTENT

- Divisibility, prime factorization, classifying whole numbers by the number of factors

TIMETABLE

- 30 minutes for activity
- 10 minutes for class discussion

ACTIVITY DISCUSSION

Following up on the previous activities, stress the important idea of the prime numbers as the building blocks of the set of whole numbers; the structure of the set is built upon the prime number base.

On #13, students may get bogged down with the numbers (2 x 3 x 3 x 7) and not think about this written as $p_1 p_2^2 p_3$. A question asking how else could the numbers be written might be helpful. In the discussion following the group work on pages, ask the class to make a general classification of the prime decomposition of integers with exactly 1-10 factors. The table below is an example of such a classification.

# of factors	prime factorization (p's stand for primes)
1	p^0
2	p^1
3	p^2
4	p^3, $p_1 p_2$
5	p^4
6	p^5, $p_1^2 p_2$
7	p^6
8	p^7, $p_1^3 p_2$, $p_1 p_2 p_3$
9	p^8, $p_1^4 p_2^2$
10	p^9, $p_1^4 p^2$

As a class verify that $p_1^3 p^2$ has exactly 8 factors. Another good item to discuss is if there are any other representations that have exactly 3 factors. How could you check this? Discuss why a prime to the nth power will always have n+1 factors [p^0 - p^n will be the factors and there are n+1 of them]. Discuss the students strategies when making and testing their *conjectures*. Many times the students will not have the understanding that numbers of the form p^n are divisible only by numbers that divide p or are powers of p. Question 19 may need to be discussed before the students work on it. Have the students discuss what strategies they might use and have them develop an outline. A possible outline might be something like the following: show that there are two representations (p^3 and $p_1 p_2$) of numbers with 4 factors and thus it is impossible to have less than two representations, then show that it is impossible to have a number with 4 factors represented any other way than these two representations.

ACTIVITY SOLUTIONS

1. answers may vary; some possibilities are: 121, 169, 289
2. answers may vary; some possibilities are: 81, 625
3. 64
4. Every number with prime factorization p^2 has exactly 3 factors.
5. It is true. A prime to the 4th power will always have 5 factors [p^0 - p^4 will be the factors and there are 5 of them].
6. This is not true when k is composite. For example, $4^4 = 256$, which has 10 factors.

7. answers will vary; some possibilities are: 75, 147, 243
8. A prime to the 5th power will always have 6 factors [p^0 - p^5 will be the factors and there are 6 of them]. Also, a number with prime factorization of $p_1^2p_2$, will have 6 factors.
9. 225 will have an odd number of factors because it is a square number, but it will have more than 3 factors since the square root (15) is not prime
10. 1, 3, 5, 15, 45, 75, 225
11. 289 has exactly 3 factors because it is a prime squared.
12. 1, 17, 289
13.

Number	Prime Factorization	Odd or Even # of Factors	Exact # of Factors
529	23•23	odd	3
126	2•3•3•7	even	12
441	3•3•7•7	odd	9
169	13•13	odd	3
11025	3•3•5•5•7•7	odd	27
841	29•29	odd	3

14. A prime to the 6th power will always have 7 factors [p^0 - p^6 will be the factors and there are 7 of them].
15. Numbers that have an odd number of factors are perfect squares.
16. Numbers that have exactly two factors are prime numbers.
17. Numbers that have exactly four factors are primes to the 3rd power or the product of two primes.
18.

Number	Prime Factorization	Exactly 4 factors?
34	2•17	yes
546	2•3•91	no
95	5•19	yes
	p•q	yes
45	3•3•5	no
	p•p•q	no
8	2•2•2	yes
27	3•3•3	yes
	p•p•p	yes

19. A possible outline might be something like the following: show that there are two representations (p^3 and p_1p_2) of numbers with 4 factors and thus it is impossible to have less than two representations, then show that it is impossible to have a number with 4 factors represented any other way than these two representations.

Notes 4.5—E-Primes

MATH CONTENT

- Factors, primes, composites

TIMETABLE

- 30 minutes for activity
- 10 minutes for class discussion

ACTIVITY DISCUSSION

This activity is good for helping the students to apply their understanding of number theory ideas. However, this activity may take a bit of time and may have to be continued as homework. Discuss the similarities and differences between primes and composites and E-primes and E-composites. Have students justify their test for determining E-primes.

ACTIVITY SOLUTIONS

1. 2, 6, 10, 14, 18, 22, 26, 30, 34, 38
2. yes, because if it is E-composite it must be able to be expressed as a product of numbers in E and if one continues to divide the number, one will eventually get to a product of E-primes
3. $8 = 2 \cdot 2 \cdot 2$; $12 = 2 \cdot 6$; $20 = 2 \cdot 10$
4. $36 = 6 \cdot 6$ and $2 \cdot 18$
5. if an even number is of the form $4n + 2$, where n is a natural number, then the number if E-prime

Notes 4.6—Twin Primes and Prime Triples

MATH CONTENT

- Prime numbers

CONNECTIONS

- Exercises and More Problems: #64

TIMETABLE

- 15 minutes for activity
- 5-10 minutes for class discussion

ACTIVITY DISCUSSION

Before the students begin working on the activity, it may be helpful to pose the following question: "Suppose I say that for any 5 consecutive integers, one of them is divisible by 5. Explain why this is true or show an example."

While students are working, pay attention to the kind of conjectures they make and how they verify their conjectures. After they have finished #1, discuss it. Before they start on #2, have the students generate ideas on how they might go about justifying the conjecture.

ACTIVITY SOLUTIONS

A conjecture concerning twin primes is that for any pair of twin primes, p and p + 2 where p ≥ 5, the integer between the two primes is a multiple of 6. [Note that 3 and 5 are not twin primes under this conjecture.] Since al primes greater than 2 are odd, all members of a pair of twin primes are odd. Thus, the integer between the two primes is even and thus a multiple of 2. In any triplet of consecutive integers, one of the integers must be a multiple of 3. Since two of the integers in these triplets are prime (and thus not a multiple of 3), the middle integer must be a multiple of 3. Hence, the middle integer is a multiple of 6.

The prime triples problem has 3, 5 and 7 as the only solution. To prove this, suppose p -2, p, and p + 2 are primes and p > 5. If p > 5, then p - 2 and p are a pair of twin primes, which are one less and one more respectively than some multiple of 6. Let p = 6n + 1. Then p + 2 = 6n + 1 + 2 = 6n + 3 = 3(2n + 1), which shows that p + 2 is not prime because it has a factor of 3. So it is impossible to have prime triples p - 2, p, p + 2 with p > 5.

An alternate but similar proof is for p - 2 and p a pair of twin primes, p - 1 must be a multiple of 3 (proven in twin prime problem). Thus, p + 2 = p - 1 + 3 must be a multiple of 3. Hence, it is impossible for p + 2 to be prime.

Notes 4.7—Divisibility Tests

MATH CONTENT

- Divisibility

MATERIALS

- Base 10 blocks (2 flats, 3 longs, 9 units per group)

CONNECTIONS

- Exercises and More Problems: #63

TIMETABLE

- 5 minutes for class discussion of divisibility and divisibility tests for 2, 5, 10
- 20 minutes of exploration of divisibility tests for 2, 4, 8, and 3
- 10-15 minutes for class discussion

ACTIVITY DISCUSSION

The key to the divisibility question is defining what we actually mean by divisibility by n [the ability to separate a number into n equal parts]. To begin the examination of divisibility, give the divisibility test for 5 and demonstrate why it works using base ten blocks on the overhead projector. [Represent different numbers with the blocks and then test whether the number is divisible by 5 through grouping by sets of 5 units. Since longs, flats, cubes and higher powers of 10 can be grouped into sets of 5 units, it is only necessary to look at the units. Thus, only numbers having 0 or 5 units will be divisible by 5.] Emphasize to the students the need to use the blocks.

Have the students use the base ten blocks to explore the divisibility tests for 2 and 10. Next have the students explore why the divisibility tests for 2, 4, 8 and 3 are valid. The students may need to be given the tests for 4, 8 and 3.

<u>For 4</u>: An integer is divisible by 4 if and only if the last two digits of the integer represent a number divisible by 4.

<u>For 8</u>: An integer is divisible by 8 if and only if the last three digits of the integer represent a number divisible by 8.

<u>For 3</u>: An integer is divisible by 3 if and only if the sum of its digits is divisible by 3.

Concerning the verification of the divisibility tests, using the base 10 blocks students can see that for a number to be divisible by 2 only the units need to be considered because the longs, flats, cubes, etc. are always divisible by 2 [units in the longs, flats and cubes can be paired off]. For a number to be divisible by 4, only the longs and units need to be considered because the flats, cubes, etc. are always divisible by 4 [units in the flats and cubes can be grouped by fours]. For a number to be divisible by 8, only the flats, longs and units need to be considered because the cubes, etc. are always divisible by 8 [units in the cube can be grouped by eights].

Another representation can be seen by writing the prime factorizations of the place values, i.e., 10 = 2 x 5, 100 = 22 x 52, 1000 = 23 x 53, etc. Now it can be seen that all digits in the 10's, 100's, 1000's place, etc. will be divisible by 2, all digits in the 100's, 1000's place, etc. will be divisible by 4, and all digits in the 1000's place, etc. will be divisible by 8.

Using the base 10 blocks to check the divisibility test for 3, the reason that summing the digits is a valid test is that for each cube there is one unit left over after grouping by threes [999 is divisible by 3], for each flat there is one unit left over [99 is divisible by 3], and for each long there is one unit left over [9 is divisible by 3]. Thus, adding the digits in a number is the same as adding one unit for each cube, flat, long, plus all the units.

A good extension is to have the students discuss how a divisibility test for 4 and 8 could be written using the idea of summing the digits in some way [for 4—take 2 times the tens digit and add the units digit; for 8—take 4 times the hundreds digit, 2 times the tens digit and add the units digit].

Notes 4.8—Divisibility in Different Bases

MATH CONTENT

- Divisibility

CONNECTIONS

- Exercises and More Problems: #80

TIMETABLE

- 20 minutes for activity
- 10 minutes for class discussion

ACTIVITY DISCUSSION
Bring out the ideas of decomposition and verification in the discussion of this activity. Have the students present their strategies for determining and verifying the divisibility tests.

ACTIVITY SOLUTIONS
1. A number is divisible by 3 in base twelve if and only if the units digit is 0, 3, 6, or 9.
2. A number is divisible by 5 in base six if and only if the sum of the digits is divisible by 5.
3. A number is divisible by 2 in base five if and only if the sum of the digits is divisible by 2.

Notes 4.9—Factors and Multiples

MATH CONTENT

- Factorization, greatest common divisor/factor, least common multiple

CONNECTIONS

- Exercises and More Problems: #81

TIMETABLE

- 15 minutes for activity
- 5-10 minutes for class discussion

ACTIVITY DISCUSSION

Bring out the ideas of *decomposition* and *generalization* in the discussion of this activity. Ask the students to share their algorithms for finding the GCD and LCM.

ACTIVITY SOLUTIONS

1. 9
2. 12
3. write the prime factorization of each and compare
4. greatest common divisor or greatest common factor
5. write the prime factorization of each number, and then take the product of all of the common factors
6. 720
7. 6300
8. write the prime factorization of each and compare
9. least common multiple
10. write the prime factorization of each number, and then take the product of all the factors but counting only common factors once

Notes 4.10—A Different Way of Counting

MATH CONTENT

- Modular arithmetic

CONNECTIONS

- Exercises and More Problems: #65

TIMETABLE

- 15 minutes for activity
- 20 minutes to make up similar problem and exchange
- 10 minutes for class discussion

ACTIVITY DISCUSSION

This problem provides students with a problem-solving situation from which will emerge the idea of modular arithmetic. It is important that the students have time to explore and grasp the essence of the problem and its solution before any introduction is given about modular arithmetic.

As groups complete the problem, have them make up a similar problem in their groups. The groups will need to decide what are the important characteristics of this type of problem. Problems will be exchanged among the groups with solutions checked by the group who created the problem. The discussion following this should bring out the common characteristics of problems of this type. Most students will not be familiar with modular arithmetic so after some discussion you can say something like, "We call this type of counting modular arithmetic. Here is a formal definition of modular arithmetic:

"For integers a and b, **a is congruent to b modulo m**, written a = b (mod m), if and only if a - b is a multiple of m, where m is a positive integer greater than 1."

Discuss how the problems relate to this definition. Note: throughout this activity students will anticipate that b, from the definition above, must be the remainder, and hence will always be ≤ a. This need not be true: a and b can be interchanged. The relationship shows congruence but not order. One way to discuss this is to say that a and b have the same remainders and so they are congruent. It is easiest to deal with smaller numbers and so it may be most convenient to have b be the remainder. However that need not be the case.

ACTIVITY SOLUTIONS

By making an organized list, such as the one below, students can keep track of which day corresponds to what number. Using the list to look for a pattern, the students can see that this method of counting is equivalent to counting on the seven days of the week and returning to the beginning (Wednesday) each time and starting over at zero. Thus to count to 969, the idea is to see that 969 divided by 7 has remainder 3 so 969 is equal to 3 (or 10) mod 7 which corresponds to Saturday (not Sunday as Nicole stated!).

Notes 4.11—Operations with Modular Arithmetic

MATH CONTENT

- Modular arithmetic

CONNECTIONS

- Exercises and More Problems: #66-68

TIMETABLE

- 20 minutes for activity
- 10 minutes for class discussion

ACTIVITY DISCUSSION

The discussion following the activity should focus on the mathematical structure of the clock arithmetic system, and modular arithmetic systems in general. The clock arithmetic activity is an excellent place to emphasize developing mathematics notation and the written description of carefully worded algorithms. The addition and multiplication tables provide a good opportunity to discuss field properties such as closure, commutativity, identities, inverses, etc.

ACTIVITY SOLUTIONS

1. keep counting around the clock; 4 o'clock; 4 o'clock
2. add a + b, divide a + b by a, look at the remainder (will be 0, 1, 2, . . . , a - 1) and that is the time it will be
3. same procedure; on the clock we use the digits 1 - 5, whereas in arithmetic mod 5 we use the digits 0-4
4.

+	0	1	2	3
0	0	1	2	3
1	1	2	3	0
2	2	3	0	1
3	3	0	1	2

x	0	1	2	3
0	0	0	0	0
1	0	1	2	3
2	0	2	0	2
3	0	3	2	1

5. a. $2 - 3 = 3$ b. $3 - 1 = 2$ c. $0 - 2 = 2$
    d. $3 \div 2 =$ not possible   e. $2 \div 3 = 2$ f. $0 \div 2 = 0$ or 2
6. there are no restrictions on subtraction; however, with division it is not always possible to find a solution; 5d is similar to dividing by zero over the set of integers because in both cases, the reason you cannot divide, is that you cannot multiply a number by the divisor to get the dividend

Notes 4.12—Mystery Numeration System

MATH CONTENT

- Prime numbers, different bases

TIMETABLE

- 20 minutes for activity
- 10 minutes for class discussion

ACTIVITY DISCUSSION

Again, the discussion following the Mystery Numeration System should focus on the mathematical structure of modular arithmetic systems in general.

ACTIVITY SOLUTIONS

The key to the Mystery Numeration System is that the prime numbers are numbered first, starting with 2 numbered as 1, 3 as 10, 5 as 100, 7 as 1000, etc. Composite numbers are then written as the sums of their prime factors [e.g., $14 = 2 \times 7$ is numbered as $1 + 1000 = 1001$]. For small values (e.g., 1-25) each numeral in this system is associated with a unique number. However, for large values this is not true. For example, 3 is written as 10, but 2_{10} is also written as 10. Each number is associated with a unique numeral in this system since each number has a unique prime factorization.

Notes 4.13—Figurate Numbers

MATH CONTENT

- Geometric representations of numbers

CONNECTIONS

- Exercises and More Problems: #69

TIMETABLE

- 15 minutes for activity
- 10 minutes for class discussion

ACTIVITY DISCUSSION

For this activity it is important that the students make generalizations for each of the representations of numbers. During the class discussion, guide the discussion towards an examination of the most concise and efficient generalizations. Also, emphasize the concept of multiple representations— these numbers are illustrated by numerals as well as geometric figures.

ACTIVITY SOLUTIONS

The generalizations for the figurate numbers can be made by considering the areas of the figures. The generalizations for triangular numbers is $n(n+1)/2$ (1/2 base • height); for square numbers -- n^2 (side squared); for oblong numbers -- $n(n+1)$ (base • height); for pentagonal numbers, divide the figure into a square and a triangle. It turns out that
$P_n = S_n + T_{n-1} = n^2 + (n-1)n/2 = n(3n-1)/2.$

Notes 4.14—Number Ideas: Proofs Without Words

MATH CONTENT

- Geometric representations of numbers

CONNECTIONS

- Exercises and More Problems: #70-72

TIMETABLE

- 15 minutes for activity
- 10 minutes for class discussion

ACTIVITY DISCUSSION

Before having students start on the activity, discuss the idea of proof and what it means in the context of mathematics. While students work on the proof on page 18, pay attention to the conjectures they make and how they initiate the development of the proof. Students may need help in going from the initial concrete visual representations to the generalized result for all integers.

ACTIVITY SOLUTIONS

The visual pattern suggests the following generalization

$$1 + 2 + 3 + ... + (n - 1) + n + (n - 1) + ... + 3 + 2 + 1 = n^2$$

This gives $2(1 + 2 + ... + (n - 1)) + n = n^2$

so that $2(1 + 2 + ... + (n - 1)) = n^2 - n$

and so $1 + 2 + ... + (n - 1) = n(n - 1)/2$

Notes 4.15—The Fibonacci Sequence

MATH CONTENT

- Number sequences

CONNECTIONS

- Exercises and More Problems: #73, 76-77

TIMETABLE

- 20 minutes for activity
- 10 minutes for class discussion

ACTIVITY DISCUSSION

You may want to have students read more about the Fibonacci sequence in other resources.

ACTIVITY SOLUTIONS

1.

# of Months	# of Rabbit Pairs
1	1
2	1
3	2
4	3
5	5
6	8

2. 1, 1, 2, 3, 5, 8, 13, 21, 34, 55, 89, 144, 233, 377, 610, 987, 1597, 2584, 4181, 6765

3. a. every third number (3rd, 6th, 9th, etc.)
    b. every fourth number (4th, 8th, 12th, etc.)
    c. every fifth number (5th, 10th, 15th, etc.)
    d. every seventh number (7th, 14th, etc.)
    e. every tenth number

4. a. adding up consecutive terms of the sequence; the sum of the first n terms is one less than the (n + 2)nd term
    b. $1 + 1 + 2 + 3 + 5 + 8 = 20$; $1 + 1 + 2 + 3 + 5 + 8 + 13 = 33$;
        $1 + 1 + 2 + 3 + 5 + 8 + 13 + 21 = 54$; $1 + 1 + 2 + 3 + 5 + 8 + 13 + 21 + 34 = 88$;
        $1 + 1 + 2 + 3 + 5 + 8 + 13 + 21 + 34 + 55 = 143$

5. no, the patterns do not hold

6. no, the patterns do not hold

Notes 4.16—Pascal's Triangle

MATH CONTENT

- Number patterns

CONNECTIONS

- Exercises and More Problems: #74-75, 83

TIMETABLE

- 15 minutes for activity
- 5-10 minutes for class discussion

ACTIVITY DISCUSSION
You may want to have students read more about Pascal's Triangle in other resources.

ACTIVITY SOLUTIONS
1. you get each term by adding the two terms on either side of it in the row above
2. next row is: 1   7   21   35   35   21   7   1
   next row is: 1   8   28   56   70   56   28   8   1
3.

Row #	Sum of Terms
1	1
2	2
3	4
4	8
5	16
6	32
7	64
8	128
9	256

the sum of the terms in a row is equal to 2^{n-1}, where n is the row number
4. 1, 1, 2, 3, 5, 8, 13, . . . which is a Fibonacci sequence
5. answers will vary

Chapter 5: Probability & Statistics

Chapter Overview:

A great many events in the world around us involve uncertainty and chance. It is easy to find examples from business, education, law, medicine, and everyday experience. Two examples come readily to mind: (1) the weather forecaster on TV says, "There is a 70% chance of rain tomorrow"; (2) with only a very small portion of votes counted, newscasters are able to project winners of political elections and final percentages of votes with considerable accuracy. How was the 70% figure obtained? How can newscasters attain such accuracy with so little information? The branches of mathematics called probability and statistics were developed to help us deal with situations involving uncertainty and chance in a precise and objective manner. In this chapter you will conduct several experiments where you will explore basic principals underlying probability and statistics.

Big Mathematical Ideas:

Data & chance, independence/dependence, representation, mathematical model

NCTM Standards Links:

K - 4:   Mathematics as problem solving; Mathematics as communication; Mathematics as reasoning; Mathematical connections; Statistics & probability

5 - 8:   Mathematics as problem solving; Mathematics as communication; Mathematics as reasoning; Mathematical connections; Statistics; Probability

Chapter Outline:

Notes 5.1—Probability Experiment I: A Spinner Experiment

MATH CONTENT

- Experimental probability, sample space

MATERIALS

- 1 spinner for each group: 3/12 Red, 9/12 Blue, sectors numbered from 0 - 9 & repeated for some numbers

CONNECTIONS

- Exercises and More Problems: #25-26, 54

TIMETABLE

- 15 minutes for activity
- 5 minutes for class discussion

ACTIVITY DISCUSSION

During the discussion of the spinner experiment, introduce the terms sample space and experimental probability and discuss these by combining data from each group. Students will be able to compare their conjectures about the outcome of 100 spins. How did more data affect the experiment? Introduce the term theoretical probability. Pose questions such as the following ones to discuss as a group:

- Would you be just as likely to spin a red 8 as a blue 8? Why?
- What do you think are the chances of spinning an even number of either color?
- What do you think are the chances of spinning a number between 3 and 8?

ACTIVITY SOLUTIONS

1. not as likely to obtain a red since there are more blue spaces
2. chances are 3 out of 12 or 1/4
3. chances are 9 out of 12 or 3/4

Notes 5.2—Probability Experiment II: What's in the Bag?

MATH CONTENT

- Experimental probability, theoretical probability

MATERIALS

- 1 color tile bag (or small, colored objects) for each group: 4 color combinations of 10 tiles

CONNECTIONS

- Exercises and More Problems: #27, 55

TIMETABLE

- 15 minutes for activity
- 10 minutes for class discussion

ACTIVITY DISCUSSION

During the discussion of "What's in the Bag?", have groups share their conjectures and reasoning when all the groups have made a prediction. Announce that they are to look in the bag and compare what they find with what they predicted. Each group should then determine the experimental and theoretical probability of drawing each color.

ACTIVITY SOLUTIONS

Solutions will be dependent upon the combinations of the four colors in each bag.

Notes 5.3—Probability Experiment III: An Experiment with Dice

MATH CONTENT

- Experimental probability, theoretical probability

MATERIALS

- 1 pair of dice for each group

CONNECTIONS

- Exercises and More Problems: #29, 35, 56

TIMETABLE

- 15 minutes for activity
- 5 minutes for class discussion

ACTIVITY DISCUSSION

During the dice experiment encourage students to develop valid or at least reasonable strategies and explanations for their conjectures. Discuss the idea of chance and how it was present in the three probability experiments. Make note of the conjectures and generalizations that were made and also the problem solving strategies that were used.

ACTIVITY SOLUTIONS

1. Possible sums include: 2, 3, 4, 5, 6, 7, 8, 9, 10, 11, 12. Their respective probabilities are: 1/36, 1/18, 1/12, 1/9, 5/36, 1/6, 5/36, 1/9, 1/12, 1/18, 1/36.
2. Probability of rolling a 7 or 11 is 8/36 = 2/9
3. Probability of not rolling a 7 or 11 is 28/36 = 7/9
4. Probability of rolling a 1 is 0. That is, it is impossible.
5. Probability of rolling a 2, 3, or 12 on the first roll is 1/9.
6. 7 is the most likely sum to occur (6 ways). The least likely sums are 2 and 12 (1 way each).
7. For experiment I the probability of drawing a sum of 12 is 6/100 = 3/50; for experiment II the probability is 5/90 = 1/16.
8. Any time the size of the sample space is changed the probability of the occurrence of an event will change.

Notes 5.4—Are These Dice Games Fair?

MATH CONTENT

* Equally likely events, fairness

MATERIALS

* 1 pair of dice for every two students, clock/watch with second hand or seconds indicator

CONNECTIONS

* Exercises and More Problems: #39, 57

TIMETABLE

* 25 minutes for activity
* 10 minutes for class discussion

ACTIVITY DISCUSSION

In the discussion of previous homework, review the dice experiment of Activity 5.3 by asking students to share some of their answers and explanations for questions 1-8. Develop a class conjecture about the probability of one event happening and then another. Come back to this conjecture at the end of the class. (This is based on the Fundamental Counting Principle—If there are m sets, the first containing n_1 elements, the second containing n_2 elements, . . ., and the mth containing n_m elements, then the number of ways to form an arrangement of m elements by selecting in order one element form each of the m sets is $n_1 \times n_2 \times \ldots \times n_m$.)

To begin this activity the students need to spend a few minutes reading and discussing games 1 and 2. It is important for them to make conjectures before playing. During the class discussion of the games, have the students compare their predictions among themselves. Ask, "What strategies would allow further verification of these outcomes?" Students could use any method which examines all possible outcomes for the purpose of comparison.

ACTIVITY SOLUTIONS

Game 1:

Difference of Two Numbers	Number of Ways It Can Occur
0	6
1	10
2	8
3	6
4	4
5	2

Counting the number of odds and evens and summing the right column entries for each, we get 18 times you get even and 18 times you get odd. Therefore, the game is fair.

<u>Game 2</u>: Simply by noting that the product of two even numbers is even, the product of even and odd is even and **only** the product of odd and odd is odd, we can conclude that the "even" player will have advantage. The game is not fair.

Notes 5.5—Basic Probability Notions

MATH CONTENT

- Conditional probability, combinations, expected value

CONNECTIONS

- Exercises and More Problems: #28, 36, 41, 58

TIMETABLE

- 25 minutes for activity
- 10 minutes for class discussion

ACTIVITY DISCUSSION

During the discussion of this activity, have students share their various diagrams and solutions. Introduce the term tree diagram and discuss its usefulness. A possible discussion could include the concept of randomness, independent/dependent events and applications of the Fundamental Counting Principle. Students may need clarification for Problems 2 c. and d. as they involve a new concept, which will force them to rely on their intuition with help from a tree diagram.

Discuss how the idea of chance was present in the activities, what conjectures and generalizations were made, and what problem solving strategies were used.

ACTIVITY SOLUTIONS

1. a. Label the 3 blue marbles B1, B2, and B3, and the 2 orange marbles O1 and O2. Then the sample space consists of the following 20 outcomes:

B1 B2	B2 B1	B3 B1	O1 B1	O2 B1
B1 B3	B2 B3	B3 B2	O1 B2	O2 B2
B1 O1	B2 O1	B3 O1	O1 B3	O2 B3
B1 O2	B2 O2	B3 O2	O1 O2	O2 O1

   b. Both marbles are orange: probability is 2/20 = 1/10.
       Neither marble is orange: probability is 6/20 = 3/10.
       At least one marble is orange: probability is 14/20 = 7/10.
   c. Probabilities might vary in the short term, but should come closer and closer to the theoretical probabilities as the amount of data grows large.

2. a. Probability is 1/9.
    b. Probability is 8/9.
    c. Probability is 6/10 = 3/5.
    d. Probability is 18/90 = 1/5.

Notes 5.6—Basic Counting Principles

MATH CONTENT

- Counting principles, combinations, permutations

MATERIALS

- one calculator per group will be useful

CONNECTIONS

- Exercises and More Problems: #30-34, 37-38, 40, 42-45, 59

TIMETABLE

- 40 minutes for activity
- 15 minutes for class discussion

ACTIVITY DISCUSSION

This activity deals with basic counting techniques that are most commonly used to solve probability and related kinds of problems. The purpose of the activities is to provide students with opportunities to build up their intuition regarding these techniques. To help fill the vacuum created by the absence of definitions, you should encourage students to try first to solve simpler problems and to draw pictures and diagrams. For example, students can answer question #1 of Situation I by first considering the case of keys with 2 notch positions and 2 depths of notch at each position and then building up to the problem as stated.

The problem involving the identical white Mustangs (#2) is not an easy one. This is why students are asked to suggest how to go about determining how likely it would be for one key to fit the locks of 2 different identical cars. A look at a small special case helps illustrate the complexity of the problem. Suppose there are only 2 types of keys (say, K_1 and K_2) and only 4 cars (C_1, C_2, C_3, and C_4). If all 4 cars were keyed alike (say with K_1), then the probability of there being 2 cars keyed alike is different than if 2 cars were keyed for K_1 and the other 2 cars were keyed for K_2. In the first case, the probability is 1, in the second the probability is 1/3.

The focus of all problems in this activity is for students to be able to recognize 4 different types of problems and the counting methods that apply to each type (see explanations of the counting types in the *Resource Manual*) It is important for students to solve several problems involving the types, so be sure to assign an appropriate number of problems from the "Exercises and More Problems" section. In general, be sure to have ample discussion of #6 for Situation I, #6 for Situation II, #5 for Situation III, and #4 and #5 for Situation IV.

ACTIVITY SOLUTIONS

Situation I

1. a. For each of the 6 notch positions, there are 6 depths. So, the solution is $6 \cdot 6 \cdot 6 \cdot 6 \cdot 6 \cdot 6 = 6^6$. So, <u>46,656</u> different keys can be made.
   b. For each of the 5 notch positions, there are 7 depths. So, the solution is $7 \cdot 7 \cdot 7 \cdot 7 \cdot 7 = 7^5$. So, <u>16,807</u> different keys can be made.
   c. In this case there are $5 \cdot 5 \cdot 5 \cdot 5 \cdot 5 \cdot 5 \cdot 5 = 5^7$. So, <u>78,125</u> different keys can be made.
   d. It would be best to install the 3rd type of lock (i.e., the one with 7 notch positions) in order to have a sufficient number of keys to have a different one for each of the 50,000 cars.

2. This is a challenging and very interesting problem to attempt to solve. A look at a small special case helps illustrate just how challenging it is. Suppose there are only 2 types of keys (say, K_1

and K_2) and only 4 cars (C_1, C_2, C_3, and C_4). If all 4 cars were keyed alike (say with K_1), then the probability of there being 2 cars keyed alike is different than if 2 cars were keyed for K_1 and the other 2 cars were keyed for K_2. In the first case, the probability is 1, in the second the probability is 1/3. So, as you can see, when there are several thousand cars and several thousand different keys the problem becomes complex. One way to approach a solution would be to solve several problems involving simpler cases (such as the one discussed here) and look to see if any sort of pattern emerges.

3. Note that the problem is really asking for how many phone numbers which can be generated with 2-digit-area-codes for the digits 0, 1, 2, ..., 9. Since the first digit cannot be zero there are 9 ways it can be chosen. Also, since the first digit of the local telephone number cannot be 0 either, there are 9 ways this digit can be chosen. There are 10 possibilities for all the other digits (since they all can be zeroes; this assumes a phone number of the form (20)-400-0000 is a valid one!). Hence, there are a total of $(9)(9)(10)^7 = 810,000,000$ phone numbers with two digits area codes that can be form. This number far exceeds the U.S. population.

4. For a 2-item quiz, $5 \cdot 5 = 25$ different answer sheets are needed.
   For a 5-item quiz, $5 \cdot 5 \cdot 5 \cdot 5 \cdot 5 = 3125$ different answer sheets are needed.

5. Order matters (e.g., 123 is different from 213) in this problem, so we can solve the problem as follows: $50 \cdot 50 \cdot 50 = 125,000$ possible "combination" locks. If we interpret the word "combination" using its mathematics meaning, a combination lock should be called a "permutation" lock.

6. One possible summary of the general counting method is as follows:
   Suppose that there are n sets, the first contains e_1 elements, the second contains e_2 elements, ..., and the nth contains e_n elements. Then the number of ways to form an arrangement of n elements by selecting in order one element from each of the n sets is
   $$e_1 \cdot e_2 \cdot \ldots \cdot e_n.$$

Situation II

1. There are $4 \cdot 3 \cdot 2 \cdot 1 = 24$ anagrams for the letters E, N, O, and P.
2. There are $6 \cdot 5 \cdot 4 \cdot 3 \cdot 2 \cdot 1 = 720$ anagrams for the letters A, E, L, P, S and T.
3. The word BANANA has 6 letters, but only 3 different letters (A, B, and N). There are at least 2 ways to solve this problems. One is to list the sample space of all possible arrangements:

AAABNN   AAANBN   AAANNB   AABANN   AABNAN   AABNNA
AANABN   AANANB   AANBAN   AANBNA   AANNAB   AANNBA
ABAANN   ABANAN   ABANNA   ABNAAN   ABNANA   ABNNAA

.
.
.

NBANAA   NBNAAA   NNAAAB   NNAABA   NNABAA   NNBAAA (There are 60.)

The other is to recognize that there are 3 A's, 2 N's, and 1 B. If we determine the number of arrangements of 6 letters, we get $6 \cdot 5 \cdot 4 \cdot 3 \cdot 2 \cdot 1 = 720$ arrangements. But, we must eliminate those arrangements that are indistinguishable from each other, so we must eliminate the duplicates contributed by the 3 A's, then eliminate the duplicates contributed by the 2 N's. In general, yet another counting principle, the <u>Distinguishable Permutations Principle</u>, states: If a set of n objects has n_1 of one kind of object, n_2 of a second kind, and so on, with $n = n_1 + n_2 + \ldots + n_i$, then the number of distinguishable permutations of the n objects is ___
$$\frac{n!}{n_1! \, n_2! \, \ldots n_i!}$$

So, we have $6!/(3!2!) = 60$ arrangements.

4. $4 \cdot 3 \cdot 2 \cdot 1 = 24$ arrangements are possible.

5. Is this a fast-pitch or a slow-pitch team? If it is fast pitch team there are 6•5•4•3•2•1 = 720 possible batting orders. If it is a slow-pitch team, there are 7•6•5•4•3•2•1 = 5040 possible batting orders.

6. Any situation would be appropriate where 4 items are to be placed in a row such that <u>order matters</u>.

Situation III

1. There are 10•9•8 = 720 ways to fill the top 3 positions of the NCBC standings.

2. a. There are at least 2 ways to interpret this question. If we assume that the best 5 floats have already been chosen, then there are 5•4•3•2•1 = 120 possible parades. (Note: Different parades are simply different arrangements of the 5 floats.) If the best 5 floats have not yet been chosen and we count different orders of appearance of the 5 floats to be different parades, then there are 10•9•8•7•6 = 30,240 possible parades. If we are interested only in the total number of different (i.e., unordered) sets of 5 floats, then there are 10•9•8•7•6 ÷ 5•4•3•2•1 = 152 such sets of floats.

    b. If we use 152 sets of 5 floats and 48 parades (24 hours per day and a parade begins every half hour) can start each day, then more than 3 days will elapse before the last parade starts out.

3. The 4 ticketed passengers can board in 24 ways (4•3•2•1). The other 6 passengers can board in 720 ways (6•5•4•3•2•1). Taken together the 10 passengers can board in 24 • 720 = 17,280 ways.

4. A main dish can be served on 10 days without repeating; 2 vegetable dishes can be served on 28 days with repeating; a dessert can be served on 13 days without repeating. Together they can serve 10 • 28 • 13 = 3,6490 meals without repeating a lunch plate.

5. With the exception of #2.a, the problems involve combinations (i.e., arrangements without regard for order; ABC is the same as CBA, for example). In exercises #3 and #4, it is possible to list all of the arrangements of a subset or subsets of the total set (e.g., in #3, the 4 ticketed passengers are a subset of the larger set of 10 passengers, and the 6 other passengers are a subset of the set of 10). Once this is done, the total number of ways to arrange the elements can be found by multiplying the ways to arrange the subsets.

Situation IV

1. 7•6•5 ÷ 3•2 = 35 committees can be selected.

2. 5•4 ÷ 2 = 10 matches will be played.

3. 6•5•4 ÷ 3•2 = 20 subsets.

4. Answers will vary. The most important thing is to be sure that the problem is realistic for elementary school students. Example: Rafer has 6 medals for sports excellence: a gold for Tae-Kwon-Do, 3 silver medals for soccer, and 2 bronze medals for archery. Every day before going to school he lines up his medals in a different way. How many consecutive days will it take for him to complete all possible line ups?

5. Answers will vary. The most important thing is to be sure that the problem is realistic for elementary school students. Luise has 5 crayons—blue, red, green, brown, and yellow—in

her backpack. Heather, Connie, and Hal asked Luise if they could borrow one crayon from her. Luise reached into her pack and drew out 3 crayons. How many different possible sets of 3 crayons could she have drawn out of her pack?

Notes 5.7—Basic Ideas of Statistics

MATH CONTENT

- Measures of central tendency, box-and-whisker plots

MATERIALS

- 1 calculator per group would be useful; a graphing calculator that can do box-and-whisker plots would be handy

CONNECTIONS

- Exercises and More Problems: #22, 60

TIMETABLE

- 30 minutes for activity
- 10 minutes for class discussion

ACTIVITY DISCUSSION

During the discussion of the activity, ask students to define median and mean.(only _descriptions_ of median and mean are provided in the activity). In what cases would it be better to use the mean as a representative average? Ask for definitions of outliers and discuss their effects. Introduce the term mode and ask the students to describe the relationships among these three concepts. During the discussion of #2, be sure to include non-quantitative issues (e.g., management wants to maximize profit and minimize expenses, whereas the workers want to maximize their salaries). It would be useful to include in this discussion attention to the popular myth, "Statistics can be interpreted anyway you want."

Pay special attention to item #5.c. on box-and-whiskers plots because it is important that students begin to think seriously about choosing representations for data that best convey the message they wish to convey.

ACTIVITY SOLUTIONS

1. <u>Mean salary</u>: $45,673.17
   <u>Range of salaries</u>: $178,000 ($200,000 - $22,000)
   <u>Median salary</u>: $36,600
   <u>First quartile salary</u>: $32,500
   <u>Third quartile salary</u>: $36,600
   <u>Interquartile range of salaries</u>: 7 salaries of $32,500 each and 14 salaries of $36,500 each are the interquartile range.
2. It is likely that management wished to keep salaries of workers as low as possible in order to maximize profits; hence they reported the mean as the average because it includes all scores, even extreme one that are not representative ones. The workers, on the other hand, chose the median because they wanted to suggest that salaries are too low.
3. The median and third quartile are the same because of the way the salaries are distributed. Notice that when the salaries are ordered from highest to lowest, the median is the middle salary (i.e., the 11th salary), which is $36,600. The third quartile is salary below which 3/4 of the salaried lie. In this case, the third quartile falls within the set of salaries earned by 16 workers—$36,600.
4. The addition of a single salary of $180,000 would raise the mean to $48,871.43 and the median would not change. The mean would rise because the mean is determined by summing all salaries and dividing by the number of salaries and the new salary is higher than the

original mean. The median would not change because both the original median, the 21st salary (in rank order), and the new median, the 22nd salary, are both $36,600.

5.   a. 7.5 is the 2nd quartile

   b. The scores 9, 8, 7, 5 are the interquartile range

   c. A box-and-whisker plot is especially good for providing a way to see how a set of data are spread out. Because it gives a 5-number summary of the data, it provides benchmarks for dividing a set of data into quartile. Perhaps most important, box-and-whisker plots are especially good for comparing two or more sets of data.

6. <u>Box-and-Whisker Plot for the Original Salary Data</u>:

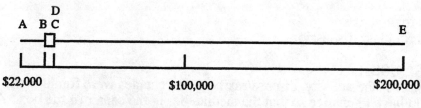

A = $22,000 (minimum salary)
B = $32,500 (1st quartile)
C = D = $36,600 (3rd quartile & median salary)
E = $200,000 (maximum salary)
E = $200,000 (maximum salary)

<u>Box-and-Whisker Plot for the Updated Salary Data:</u>

The box-and-whisker plot does not change at all with the addition of a single salary of $180,000. Hence, there is no need to change the answer given in #3.

Notes 5.8—Exploring Unpaired Data: More on Box-and-Whisker Plots

MATH CONTENT

- Measures of central tendency, box-and-whisker plots, unpaired data

MATERIALS

- 1 calculator per group would be useful; a graphing calculator that can do box-and-whisker plots would be handy

TIMETABLE

- 20 minutes for activity
- 10 minutes for class discussion

ACTIVITY DISCUSSION

During the discussion of the activity, discuss/ask how percentages were found in #2. Discuss #4 and how data would have to change so that the median lies in the center of the box. Ask groups for descriptions for #7. Engage the students in discussing what is meant by unpaired data and how that might be different from paired data.

Discuss how the idea of multiple representations was present in Activities 5.7 and 5.8, and how the concept of generalization might be involved. What is the difference between generalization and inference? What does it mean to make inferences? How can we determine if our inferences are valid? Can there be two inferences made from the same data set that are both valid but that support different positions? Have the students discuss what can be meant by the term average. Encourage students to think about what average means in their everyday usage.

ACTIVITY SOLUTIONS

1.

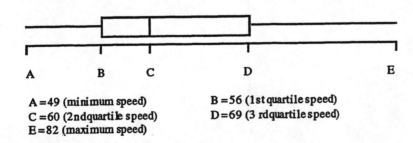

A = 49 (minimum speed)   B = 56 (1st quartile speed)
C = 60 (2nd quartile speed)   D = 69 (3rd quartile speed)
E = 82 (maximum speed)

2. a. 50%
    b. 24%
    c. 68%
    d. 52%
    e. 24% on the left (lower) whisker; 24% on the right (upper) whisker
3. Yes, the right whisker is longer, indicating that the speeds outside the box are more widely spread out on that whisker than on the other one.
4. The median is not in the center of the box because the speeds are not evenly (equally) distributed within the entire set of speeds. In fact, the speeds are a bit more clustered at the lower end of the ordering of the speeds.

5. 24% (i.e., those whose speeds were above the upper quartile of 69 mph).

6. The data set is considered unpaired data because the speeds have not been associated with (i.e., paired with) any other set of data, such as time of day, weather conditions, day of the week, etc.

7. If the data had been paired with time of day on a weekday, then the speeds would take on new meanings. For example, a speed of 71 mph at 6 am might be more likely than the same speed at 8 am on the same day.

8. Assume that the posted speed limit is 65 mph. Most drivers drive within the legally accepted maximum limit of 70 mph. In fact, more than 3/4 (specifically, 76%) of all drivers drive at speeds less than the accepted limit. Furthermore, slightly more than half (specifically, 52%) of the drivers drive between 56 and 69 mph, and more than half of all drivers drive at a speed less than or equal to 60 mph. Finally, one-quarter of all drivers still drive less than the old maximum speed limit of 55 mph.

Notes 5.9—Exploring Unpaired Data: Histograms

MATH CONTENT

- Frequency, histograms, unpaired data

MATERIALS

- No special materials are necessary, although graph paper or centimeter grid paper would come in handy, as would calculators.

CONNECTIONS

- Exercises and More Problems: #48-53

TIMETABLE

- 30 minutes for activity
- 10 minutes for class discussion

ACTIVITY DISCUSSION

In helping students understand how to construct histograms, be sure to pay special attention to the fact that data used to create a histogram must first be grouped into equal-sized intervals of their choosing. Refer to the Bureau of Census example to make this point. The decision to group the data into 10-year intervals was not random, but was based on a desire to make it easy to make comparisons across intervals. Ask students how else the population might have been grouped and what would have been the problem with grouping the data into intervals of unequal size. This discussion will lead nicely into the activity involving Per Pupil Expenditures on Schools.

In discussing students' histograms for the per pupil expenditures activity, pay particular attention to their choice of intervals and the types of predictions they have about the effect of changing the intervals. Relate this discussion to the earlier discussion about non-quantitative issues that influence decisions about statistical data.

ACTIVITY SOLUTIONS
1.

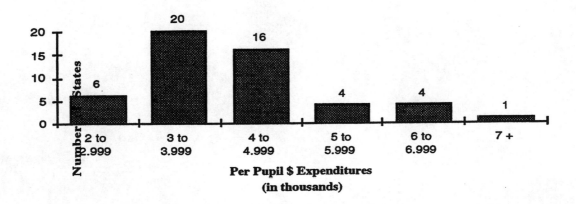

2. Questions that can be answered depend on the nature of the histogram created. Note, for example, that the graph displayed above does not provide any answers to questions about comparisons of states by geographic location (e.g., Southern states vs. Northern states, or states east of the Mississippi River vs. west of the Mississippi River). It does provide answers to the follow types of questions:
    a. Where does the median per pupil expenditure fall? (*ans.* Between $3,000 and $3,999)
    b. How many states spend at least $5,000 per pupil? (*ans.* 9)
    c. What is the most common range of per pupil expenditures? (*ans.* $3,000 to $3,999)
    These questions are easily answered with only a casual look at the graph.
3. Predictions will vary considerably depending on the type of histogram made. In the histogram shown above if each interval were divided in half (e.g., if the interval 3 $3,000 to $3,999 were split into $2,000 to $2,499 and $2,500 to $2,999), there would be little effect on the types of information readily apparent from looking at the graph. However, if intervals were collapsed, the effect might be to eliminate the differences.
4. Answers will vary depending on the nature of the histogram made originally. If the original histogram shown above were re-scaled by collapsing intervals so that there were only 4 intervals as shown below, the differences among states has indeed been obscured somewhat.

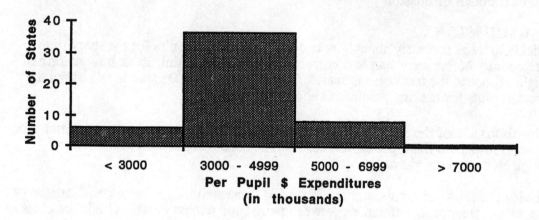

5.

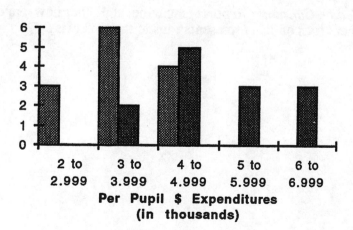

Notice that the distribution of Northeast states is essentially shifted up the scale of per pupil expenditures. The highest expenditures for the Southeastern states is only an average amount by comparison with the Northeastern states. Plotting both histograms on the same set of axes makes it much easier to compare the states in the two geographic areas.

Notes 5.10—Exploring Paired Data: Scatter Plots

MATH CONTENT

- Scatter plots, paired data

MATERIALS

- No special materials are necessary, although graph paper or centimeter grid paper would come in handy, as would calculators.

CONNECTIONS

- Exercises and More Problems: #46-47

TIMETABLE

- 20 minutes for activity
- 10 minutes for class discussion

ACTIVITY DISCUSSION

Encourage students to think seriously about how to construct the scatter plot for the study time versus test score activity before they start to construct it. Ask them to think about how scaling of their graphs might influence the message the scatter plot might convey. Be sure to talk about the limitations of scatter plots for making predictions about the future.

At the end of the discussion of the activities have students discuss differences between scatter plots and histograms with respect to the types of data each can be used with, as well as the kind of useful information each type provides.

Discuss how the idea of multiple representations is used in these activities, what generalizations or inferences the students made, and differences between paired and unpaired data. Guide the class in agreeing upon definitions for unpaired and paired data.

Ask students to bring copies of *USA Today*, *Consumer Reports* magazine, and other newspapers and magazines containing graphs or other kinds of data representations to the next class.

ACTIVITY SOLUTIONS
1.

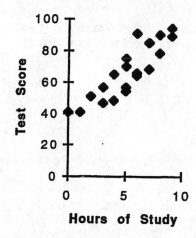

Manatees Killed by Boats

1.

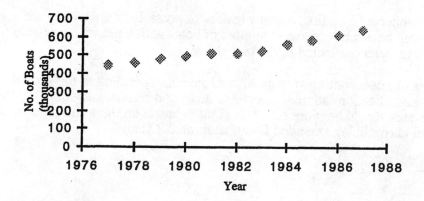

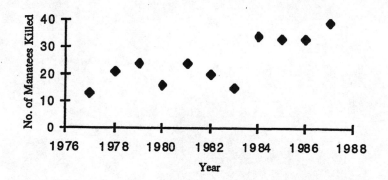

There appears to be a strong relationship between the increase in power boats and the number of manatees killed per year. As the number of boats increased over time, the number of deaths also increased. However, the drop in number of deaths in 1980 and 1983 makes it difficult to suggest that the number of deaths is due solely to the increase in number of boats.

2. The pattern suggests that if there were 550,000 boats, there would be about 30 or so deaths (if one accepts the relationship as a strong linear one). However, since there were only 15 deaths when there were 526,000 boats, it is difficult to be very confident in this prediction.

3. Scatter plots for the data are given above with "year" as the independent variable. If year is ignored, and number of boats is the independent variable, the scatter plot is as follows:

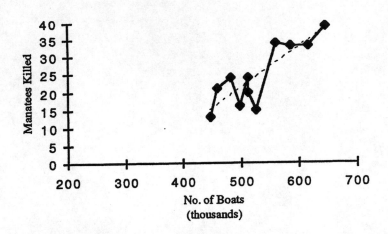

4. The data points could be connected by a line, thereby making it possible to see clearly the fluctuation in the relationship between increase in number of boats and increase in manatee deaths. The data points have been connected in the plot above.

5. Assuming that the number of boats continued to grow at a rate corresponding to the growth in the mid-1980s and assuming a linear relationship between boats and deaths, an estimate of the number of deaths of manatees would be more than 60. (This is based on the trend line shown as a dashed line in the plot above being extended for an additional 8 years.)

Notes 5.11—Statistics and Sampling

MATH CONTENT

- Statistics and sampling methods, representations and analysis of data

MATERIALS

- A collection of newspapers and magazines containing graphs and other data representations for use with the final activity. Graph paper or centimeter grid paper would come in handy, as would calculators.

CONNECTIONS

- Exercises and More Problems: #61

TIMETABLE

- 45 minutes for activity
- 10 minutes for class discussion

ACTIVITY DISCUSSION

Have students share their responses to the two questions about the two sampling examples. Ask how the groups decided if samples were biased and if they think sampling results are intended to convey certain meanings. Discuss how to make a sample as random and unbiased as possible.

Ask groups to share and compare answers to #2 d. and especially #3 of the Market Research activity—possible sources of error in data collection methods.

During the discussion of what the students found by searching through the newspapers and magazines in their search for misleading data, have students share their responses with the class. They should be able to identify at least one source of error or bias in their chosen graph or tell why it seems reasonable.

Discuss how the ideas of multiple representations, generalization, and inference were present in the activities. Have students discuss how the concept of average is present in the idea of statistical sampling, as in "the average person."

ACTIVITY SOLUTIONS

1. Discrepancies can be attributed to various phenomena including differences in the persons surveyed (e.g., Were TV viewers who were phoned as knowledgeable about the President's plan as those who participated in the survey?) Also, there may have been big differences in the way the respondents were selected for the TV poll and those who participated in the survey.

2. Persons who chose to write to Ann Lander's are more likely to have had very strong feelings about the question than those who did not. This example, points out a serious limitation in depending on volunteer participants to be representative of the population as a whole.

Market Research

1. a. Of course, people without telephones as well as those with unlisted numbers will not be represented at all. Among those in the latter group are roommates in apartments in which the telephone is in only one roommate's name. In addition, children living at home and many elderly people living with their children and without their own phones will not be represented. Finally, and perhaps most important, many spouses might not be included in the directories.

    b. Telephone directories can be supplemented by voter registration lists, automobile registration lists, and other publicly accessible lists.

    c. The results of surveys taken using telephone directories for sampling might be representative if everyone in a household held views similar to (or looked much the same as) those of the person in the sample, but might be very unrepresentative if this were not the case.

    d. There are various acceptable answers to this question.

2. a. $200/500 = 2/5 = 40\%$

    b. $200/2000 = 1/10 = 10\%$

    c. This is a probability sample because each of the 2000 males had the same chance (1/10) of being chosen and each of the 500 females had the same chance (2/5) of being chosen. Since the sample was apparently done randomly, the sampling was not done in a purposive manner.

    d. Had the sampling been done in a way to represent the proportions of male and female faculty, there would have been 4 times as many men polled as females. So, the men's views should have been given 4 times the weight as the female's. Had this been done the conclusion would have been something like: "Based on a sample, we conclude that 42% of the total faculty feel that female faculty members are underpaid relative to males." Better still, the conclusion could have been: "Based on a sample, we conclude that 30% of the male faculty feel that female faculty members are underpaid relative to males and 90% of the female feel that they are underpaid."

3. a. Diary method
    Advantages: Provides detailed and very complete viewing data if the record keeper is honest and conscientious.
    Disadvantages: Very time-consuming for the participant. Some household members might not want to be involved in the data keeping. Source of error could be lax record keeping or failure to be conscientious in recording. Data can be "manufactured" easily without there being any way to check on its accuracy.

    b. Roster-recall method
    Advantages: Easy to collect data from respondents.
    Disadvantages: may not be an accurate indicator of a viewer's typical viewing habits. For example, a person might have been out of town for some reason for a part of the week being considered, thereby causing her to miss watching some regularly viewed programs. The respondent might not be willing to admit that he or she watches certain programs.

    c. Telephone-coincidental method
    Advantages: Relatively easy to collect data and should provide current information on viewing habits. Samples can be drawn at random, thereby increasing the chances of obtaining a sample that is representative of the population.
    Disadvantages: The method is intrusive. Some persons might resent being phoned during TV watching time (or for some other reason). There is no way to know for certain that the person has provided accurate information. Also, some people do not answer their telephone while they are watching favorite programs.

    d. Automatic recorder method
    Advantages: Easy method for collecting information. Provides complete data.
    Disadvantages: The fact that a TV is turned on does not guarantee that it is being watched, not does it provide information as to how many persons are watching. This method may be the most expensive method of the four.

Method A is the best to use if respondents agree to be diligent in keeping their diaries and in recording as much information as possible. None of the methods eliminates falsification of information and this is no more a disadvantage with method A than with the others.

Chapter 6: Fraction Models & Operations

Chapter Overview:

Many real-world situations require the use of fractions. The primary purpose of this chapter is to extend your sense of fractions and your understanding of operations on fractions. Because a deep understanding of fractions is essential for anyone who will teach fraction concepts and procedures to children, the first several activities involve considerations of various ways to interpret and model (that is, represent) fractions. Then, in addition to activities aimed at helping you develop better fraction sense, the chapter moves on to investigations involving fraction computations and everyday applications of fractions.

Big Mathematical Ideas:

> problem-solving strategies, conjecturing, verifying, decomposing, generalizing, using language & symbolism, mathematical structure

NCTM Standards Links:

K - 4: Mathematics as problem solving; Mathematics as communication; Mathematics as reasoning; Mathematical connections; Number sense and numeration; Fractions & decimals

5 - 8: Mathematics as problem solving; Mathematics as communication; Mathematics as reasoning; Mathematical connections; Number & number relationships

Chapter Outline:

Notes 6.1—Introducing the Region Model

MATH CONTENT

- Concept of fraction, area, region model

MATERIALS

- Envelopes with 15 pieces (one set per group)

CONNECTIONS

- Exercises and More Problems: #43

TIMETABLE

- 10 minutes for activity
- 5 minutes for class discussion

ACTIVITY DISCUSSION

Introduce the fraction chapter by mentioning that the chapter activities will focus on the fundamental concepts of fractions. Also mention that for the first set of activities concerning fractions three different models of fractions will be used: the region model (continuous model), the linear model (i.e., a number line), the set model (discontinuous model).

Make enough copies of the squares on the next page for each group. Cut out and put pieces 1-3 in one envelope, 4-6 in another, and so on. Distribute the envelopes to the groups and have students read the directions on Activity 6.1. During the class discussion following the activity have different groups justify the fractional values they found for the pieces of the squares. Bring out the idea of *decomposition* as evident in breaking down the unit square into different pieces that total one.

ACTIVITY SOLUTIONS

1. Five squares can be formed as shown below.

2. The value of each piece is as follows:

#1 = 1/8	#2 = 1/4	#3 = 1/2
#4 = 1/4	#5 = 1/4 + 1/8 = 3/8	#6 = 1/8
#7 = 3/4 - 1/8 = 6/8 - 1/8 = 5/8	#8 = 3/8	#9 = 1/4
#10 = 1/4 + 1/8 = 3/8	#11 = 6/8 = 3/4	#12 = 1/8
#13 = 1/8	#14 = 1/2	#15 = 1/4

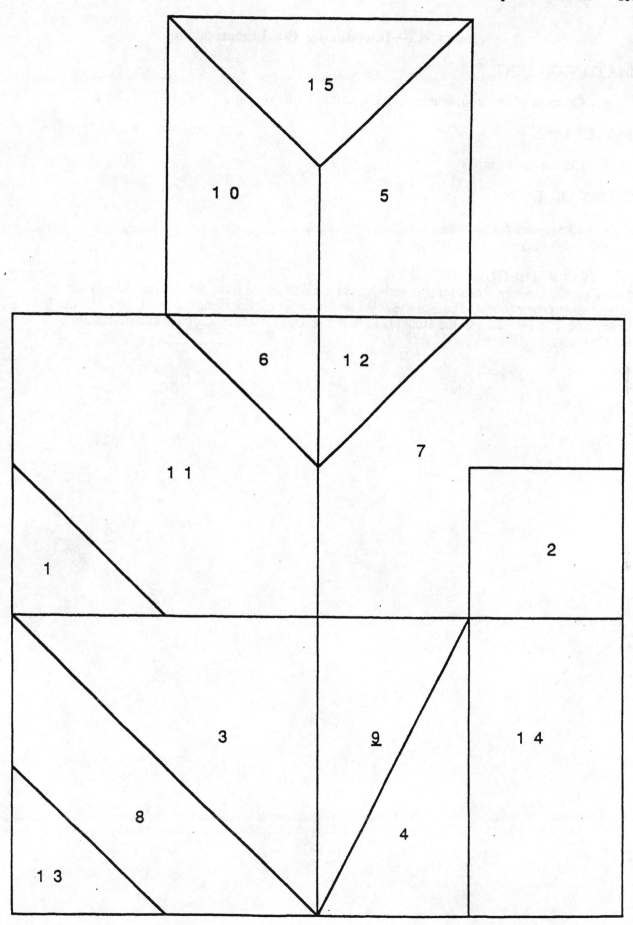

Notes 6.2—Introducing the Linear Model

MATH CONTENT

- Concept of fraction, linear model, fractional relationships

MATERIALS

- Cuisenaire rods

TIMETABLE

- 15 minutes for activity
- 5 minutes for class discussion

ACTIVITY DISCUSSION

Distribute Cuisenaire Rods for this activity. In the discussion have the students justify the relationships they found. If all of the relationships are unit fractions (i.e., 1/3, 1/4, 1/5, etc.) instead of 2/3, 3/4, etc. ask the students to find a rod that is 2/3 of another; one that is 5/6 of another, etc.

Notes 6.3—Introducing the Set Model

MATH CONTENT

- Concept of fraction, set model, fractional relationships

TIMETABLE

- 25 minutes for activity
- 10 minutes for class discussion

ACTIVITY DISCUSSION

It is likely that several groups will have different solutions for the Condominium Problem. Some students may use the method of *guess and check* to zero in on an answer, others may make an *organized list* and try to discover an answer that makes sense for both the men and the women. During the class discussion have the students share their solutions and their method of solving the problem.

After solutions have been shared, try to get the students to form a *generalization* about the relationship between the number of men and women [i.e., 2/3 m = 3/5 w or m = 9/10 w]. Then have the students **graph this relationship.** Many groups will graph a continuous line rather than integral ordered pairs. This is important to bring up during the class discussion (Is it possible to have part of a person?).

ACTIVITY SOLUTIONS

Four possible solutions are provided here.

(1) Draw a picture. Keep drawing sets of women and men until you reach a point where the number of married men and women are equal. [Circles indicate married individuals.]

		married
Ⓜ Ⓜ M	Ⓦ Ⓦ Ⓦ W W	2 men and 3 women
Ⓜ Ⓜ Ⓜ		4 men and 3 women
	Ⓦ Ⓦ Ⓦ W W	4 men and 6 women
Ⓜ Ⓜ Ⓜ		6 men and 6 women

Total of 9 men and 10 women ⟶ 19 people
6 married men and 6 married women ⟶ 12 people

Thus, 12/19 of the residents are married.

(2) Recognize that you need to keep to the ratios given, but you need equal numbers of married and women. So you need **common numerators** for 2/3 and 3/5. Since the least common multiple of the numerators (2 and 3) is 6, rewrite the fractions

2/3 = 6/9 and 3/5 = 6/10.

Thus, you have 6 married men and 6 married women (12 married people) out of 9 men total and 10 women total (19 people). So 12/19 of the residents are married.

(3) Write equations. Then pick an appropriate number to generate a solution.

2/3 m = 3/5 w ⟶ m = 9/10 w
Let w = 10, then m = 9 ⟶ total number of people is 19
2/3 (9) = 6 married men and 3/5 (10) = 6 married women ⟶ 12 married people

Thus, 12/19 of the residents are married.

(4) Guess and check. Pick a number for the number of married couples. [Choose one that is "nice"—that has enough factors that it is likely to work out.]

Suppose 60 couples are married. Then 2/3 m = 60 so m = 90. 3/5 w = 60 so w = 100. The total number of people is 190 and the total number of married persons is 120. Thus, 120/190 or 12/19 of residents are married.

Notes 6.4—Exploring Fraction Ideas through the Region Model

MATH CONTENT

- Concept of fraction, equal part of a whole, region model

MATERIALS

- cut out shapes from page 170

TIMETABLE

- 20 minutes for activity
- 15 minutes for class discussion

ACTIVITY DISCUSSION

To begin the activity, have the students take the two strips and tear one into two pieces and one into three pieces. Tell them to compare their strips with other group members' and note the similarities and differences. Then have them use the squares, rectangles, hexagons and circles to divide the shapes into halves and thirds, following the steps below. Page 171 should be used to record the divisions.

(1) Divide the shape by folding it, along lines of symmetry, into congruent pieces.

(2) Divide the shape by cutting (not on lines of symmetry) into congruent pieces. Verify that you have divided the shape into halves (or thirds) by placing the pieces on top of each other.

(3) Divide the shape by drawing straight lines which separate it into equal-area non-congruent parts.

Some illustrations of the divisions in step (2) are provided below.

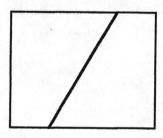 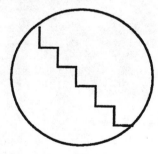

Some illustrations of the divisions in step (3) are provided below.

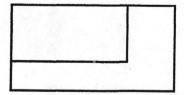 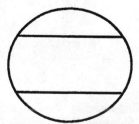

Especially for the divisions into equal-area non-congruent parts, it is important to discuss how you could decide whether or not the shape is divided into halves (or thirds). Some possible answers are to make the shape out of a heavier material and then weigh the divided pieces separately.

Another way is to use grid paper to approximate the area of each part. A third way is to use the formulas for area and calculate the area of each part.

#7 is an important question concerning the *generalization*. If no group has made the generalization, guide the students by presenting examples of cutting the square in half with lines that are not lines of symmetry [the generalization is that any line through the center of the square will cut the square in half].

Notes 6.5—Fractions on the Square: A Game using the Region Model

MATH CONTENT

- Concept of fraction, equivalent fractions, comparing fractions, region model

MATERIALS

- Two spinners for each group

TIMETABLE

- 15 minutes for activity
- 5 minutes for class discussion

ACTIVITY DISCUSSION

In the discussion of Fractions on the Square, ask the students what mathematics is involved in the game. The class should be able to generate a list including conversion of fractions to common denominators, equivalent fractions, ordering fractions, and comparing fractions. The discussion of equivalent fractions can focus on why $6/8 = 12/16$ and include mention of the multiplicative identity (multiplying by 2/2).

Notes 6.6—Fraction Puzzles using the Region Model

MATH CONTENT

- Concept of fraction, area, region model

MATERIALS

- Pattern blocks

TIMETABLE

- 15 minutes for activity
- 10 minutes for class discussion

ACTIVITY DISCUSSION

For Fraction Puzzles with Pattern Blocks students may use the method of guess and check to discover a combination of blocks that will form the desired figure. When groups are sharing their solutions, ask for another solution that meets the same conditions. At this point, discuss how knowing the ratios of the different colors to the whole figure can allow the formation of infinitely many figures meeting the same conditions [the ratios must be in terms of a common block, e.g., triangle].

Look back at the past activities using the region model and ask how the ideas of *multiple representations* [halves of a region can be shown in many ways, the fraction puzzle figures can be represented in different ways as long as the ratios are maintained—see discussion below] and *decomposition* [breaking the puzzle figures into parts according to color] are present.

Notes 6.7—Looking for Patterns with the Linear Model

MATH CONTENT

- Concept of fraction, fractional relationships, linear model

MATERIALS

- Cuisenaire rods

CONNECTIONS

- Exercises and More Problems: #42, 44

TIMETABLE

- 15 minutes for activity
- 10 minutes for class discussion

ACTIVITY DISCUSSION

When discussing this activity, have groups justify their generalization [the number of trains that can be made is $2n-1$ where n is the length in centimeters of the block—the white block is 1 cm, the red is 2 cm, etc.] and attempt to explain why the number of trains doubles as 1 cm in length is added. During this discussion ask the students how the idea of multiple representations fits in here. The Trains activity is a link between rational number ideas and number theory ideas. Rational number ideas are present in that the fractional relationships between the rods can be used in forming the trains. #42 in Exercises and More Problems uses single-color trains to bring in factors of the whole-number lengths of rods.

Notes 6.8—Exploring Fraction Ideas through the Linear Model

MATH CONTENT

- Concept of fraction, linear model, multiplication and division of fractions, number theory ideas represented in fractional relationships

MATERIALS

- cut out strips from page 177

CONNECTIONS

- Exercises and More Problems: #47

TIMETABLE

- 45-50 minutes for activity, interspersed with class discussion

ACTIVITY DISCUSSION

Some of the key things in this activity are (a) the representation of a fraction in two different ways [2/3 can be 2 of 1/3 or 1/3 of 2], (b) the representation of multiplication with strips of paper and on a number line, and (c) the representation of every number in more than one way [equivalent fractions.

The students will have difficulty with modeling 2/3 with strip #2 (#5). They will try to show 2/3 of the strip rather than 2/3 given that strip #1 is one unit. The idea is that taking **1/3 of strip #2 is equal to 2/3 because 1/3 of 2 is 2/3.** Likewise, 3/4 can be modeled by taking 1/4 of strip #3 because 1/4 of 3 is 3/4. 4/5 can be modeled by taking 1/5 of strip #4 because 1/5 of 4 is 4/5. Note: It is not easy to fold a strip into fifths, but by this time the students should have the idea and be able to draw the divisions, if not actually fold them.

Encourage the students to *generalize* the process of representing fractions in *multiple* ways in #8. The two ways are as follows: (1) a given fraction, m/n for m and n integers, can be represented as m/n of 1, or (2) m/n can be represented as 1/n of m. Discuss the different processes being used in #12—how 3 x 1/4 is different 1/4 x 3.

ACTIVITY SOLUTIONS

1. fold strip into thirds and cover two sections
2. fold strip into fourths and cover three sections; fold two strips into halves and cover three sections
4. 2 units, 3 units, 4 units
5. fold strip into thirds and cover one section; 1/3 • 2 = 2/3
6. fold strip #3 into fourths and cover one section; 1/4 • 3 = 3/4
7. fold strip #1 into fifths and cover four sections; 4/5 • 1 = 4/5; fold strip #4 into fifths and cover one section; 1/5 • 4 = 4/5
8. a given fraction, m/n for m and n integers, can be represented as m/n of 1, or m/n can be represented as 1/n of m
9. 3/4 pound
10. 3/4 pound
11. 3/4 • 1 = 3/4 and 1/4 • 3 = 3/4
12. a. start with #1 strip, fold into fourths, cover one section, have 1/4, then take 3 of those sections so have 3/4
    b. start with #3 strip, fold into fourths, cover one section, have 3/4

c. start with #1 strip, fold into fourths, cover one section, have 1/4, then fold this section into thirds so that folds are perpendicular to first folds (will probably have to fold whole strip into twelfths, in the section that representing 1/4, take 1/3 of that section, have 1/12

d. start with #1 strip, fold into thirds, cover one section, have 1/3, then fold this section into fourths so that folds are perpendicular to first folds (will probably have to fold whole strip into twelfths, in the section representing 1/3, take 1/4 of that section, have 1/12

Notes 6.9—Exploring the Density of the Set of Real Numbers

MATH CONTENT

- Density of the set of real numbers, equivalent fractions

MATERIALS

- cut out strips from page 177, two sheets of paper taped together end-to-end

TIMETABLE

- 15 minutes for activity
- 5 minutes for class discussion

ACTIVITY DISCUSSION

Have the students verify their conjecture concerning the density of the set of rational numbers during the class discussion.

ACTIVITY SOLUTIONS

2. yes
3. could use the #1 strip, fold it into half, and then fold it into thirds
4. 1/6 would be between 0 and 1/4
5. 3/6 is equivalent to 1/2
6. no
7. If you have a fraction of the form 1/n, it will be possible to use a certain number of 1/n's to represent the same number as 1/2 when n is a multiple of 2
8. 12, 6, 8
9. yes, every number can be represented as an equivalent fraction
10. yes, 4/3 is one such number
11. yes, 19/12 is one such number
12. Between any two numbers, there exists another number.

Notes 6.10—Exploring Fraction Ideas through the Set Model

MATH CONTENT

- Set models, multiplication of fractions

MATERIALS

- 12 color tiles for each group

TIMETABLE

- 10 minutes for activity
- 5 minutes for class discussion

ACTIVITY DISCUSSION

Have the students share and justify their solutions. Discuss differences between multiplication and division with the set model (e.g., color tiles) and with the linear model (e.g., strips).

ACTIVITY SOLUTIONS

1. 8
2. 9
3. 6
4. 10
5. 4
6. 3

The illustration of division of fractions with set models depends upon the numbers used. For example, 3/4 ÷ 1/4 cannot be done if the original set has 12 objects because 3/4 of 12 is 9 and 9 objects cannot be separated into groups of 4 without cutting some of the objects.

Notes 6.11—Solving Problems using the Set Model

MATH CONTENT

- Set models, operations with fractions

TIMETABLE

- 10 minutes for activity
- 5 minutes for class discussion

ACTIVITY DISCUSSION

Encourage students to draw illustrations and be systematic to help them in solving the problems.

ACTIVITY SOLUTIONS

Students might use strategies such as draw a picture , guess and check, making an organized list, or writing an equation to solve these problems. Some possible solutions are provided below.

#1
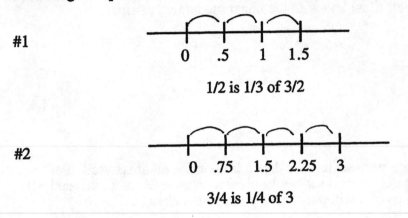

0   .5   1   1.5

1/2 is 1/3 of 3/2

#2

0   .75   1.5   2.25   3

3/4 is 1/4 of 3

#3

3/4 of # of quilts	# of quilts
.75	1.5
1.5	2.25
2.25	3

3/4 of 3 + 3/4 = 3

#4
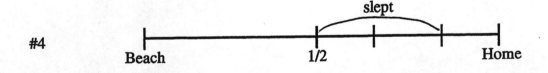

slept

Beach   1/2   Home

Samuel slept 2/3 of 1/2 of the trip = 1/3 of the trip

Notes 6.12—Classifying Problems by Operation: Revisiting Activity 3.3

MATH CONTENT

- Arithmetic operations with fractions

TIMETABLE

- 15 minutes for activity
- 10 minutes for class discussion

ACTIVITY DISCUSSION

Before beginning the activity, have the students review the operation types identified in Activity 3.3. these can be written in the blanks on Activity 6.12 at this time. Then have the students generate problem situations for these types using fractions. There are several ways of doing this: (a) have all groups make one problem for each type (this will take some time), or (b) assign two problems to each group, making sure that all the types are covered. Following the activity, have different groups share their problems and justify why the problem into a certain category (e.g., repeated addition, sharing division). Note: Sharing division only makes sense if the divisor is a whole number.

As a follow up to this activity, you may want to have the students make up fraction problems for each type of fraction model (region, linear, set), one for each operation, as a homework assignment.

ACTIVITY SOLUTIONS

answers will vary

Notes 6.13—Illustrating Operations with Region, Linear and Set Models

MATH CONTENT

- Modeling operations on fractions, equal parts of a whole

CONNECTIONS

- Exercises and More Problems: #47

TIMETABLE

- 30 minutes for activity
- 15 minutes for class discussion

ACTIVITY DISCUSSION

For this activity, it is important that the students explore how to illustrate the action taking place in the problems. It is also important that the mathematical expressions are written correctly. For example, #4 is showing 2/3 of 1/2 not 1/2 of 2/3. The difference between these two is emphasized in #7 and #8 where the resulting area (shaded region) will be the same for both if the original strips are equivalent in size, but the action of the operation will be different. The first step in #7 will be to fold the strip into sevenths and shade two. Then fold those in half to get the resulting area. For #8, the first step is to fold the strip in half, then that region into sevenths and shade two of the sevenths.

The first two pages of Activity 6.13 deal mainly with multiplication while the third page is concerned with division. These division problems can help the students begin to understand why the rule for division of fractions is to invert the second fraction and multiply.

Discuss the implicit assumption of equal parts when doing operations (e.g., 4/7 of something, what does that mean? What do you know about the 4 parts? About the 7 parts?)

ACTIVITY SOLUTIONS

1. 1/2
2. 5/3
3. 2/3
4. 2/3 of 1/2
5. 3/5 of 1/3
6. 1/3 of 3/5
7. divide unit into sevenths, shade two, then take 1/2 of the shaded part; 1/7
8. divide unit into halves, shade one, then take 2/7 of the shaded part; 1/7
9. 8/5
10. 1
11. 4
12. 88
13. 6
14. 69
15. 2
16. 3
17. 2 and 1/4
18. division is the number of times a number is contained in another number; if the rational numbers have a common denominator, then only the numerators need to be considered when trying to find the number of times a number is contained in another number
19. 15/14

Notes 6.14—Developing Fraction Sense with Linear Models

MATH CONTENT

- Using number sense with fractions

CONNECTIONS

- Exercises and More Problems: #46

TIMETABLE

- 30 minutes for activity
- 15 minutes for class discussion

ACTIVITY DISCUSSION

This activity involves the students in using estimation and logical reasoning about operations performed on rational numbers. For #1, students should be able to classify the fractions as less than 1, equal to 1, or greater than 1. Students should not compute the answers for #4. They should use estimation strategies to place the estimate on the number line.

ACTIVITY SOLUTIONS

1. a. > 1 b. < 1 c. > 1 d. < 1
   e. > 1 f. < 1
2. a. a/c   b. a/b   c. a/c
3. a. C   b. E   c. D   d. 15   e. 27
4. a. 1/4 of way between 1 and 2 (5/4)
   b. 1/4 of the way between 0 and -1 (-1/4)
   c. little to the left of 1/2 (3/8)
   d. 2/3 of way between 0 and 1 (2/3)
5. a. 1/9, 1/98, 1/987, 1/9876, . . ., 1/987654320
   b. 9/2, 98/2, 987/2, 9876/2, . . ., 987654310/2
   answers may vary for the following
   c. 98760/54321
   d. 54321/98760
   e. 87531/96420
   f. 1/12
   g. 87/96
   h. $8.75
   i. $6.75

Notes 6.15—Using the Region Model to Illustrate Multiplication

MATH CONTENT

- Multiplication with fractions, region model

CONNECTIONS

- Exercises and More Problems: #45

TIMETABLE

- 10 minutes for activity
- 5 minutes for class discussion

ACTIVITY DISCUSSION
Have students share and justify their solutions.

ACTIVITY SOLUTIONS
1. $1/4 \cdot 16 = 4$
2. $1/4 \cdot 2/3 = 1/6$
3. $1/6 \cdot 3 = 1/2$
4. $1/6 \cdot 12 = 2$
5. $1/4 \cdot 9 = 9/4$

Notes 6.16—Using the Region Model to Illustrate Division

MATH CONTENT

- Division with fractions, region model

TIMETABLE

- 20 minutes for activity
- 10 minutes for class discussion

ACTIVITY DISCUSSION
This activity engages students in problem solving and applying division ideas.

ACTIVITY SOLUTIONS
To explore the division of a rectangle into non-congruent pieces with equal area students might draw a picture and use the strategy of guess and check. An example of how the halving of the rectangle could be done is as follow:

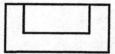

A generalization might be a statement like, "Shortening the horizontal edge of the outside portion necessitates the shortening of the vertical edge of the inside portion."

The key to the cake problem is to realize that if the five pieces have equal area and the cuts are perpendicular to the top then each of the pieces have the same amount of frosting on top. The main problem, then, is to have each piece have the same amount of frosting on the vertical sides. The solution can be more easily found by dividing the square cake into 25 units (5 x 5). Then each piece must have an area of 5 units and 4 units of the perimeter of the cake.

One solution can be found by starting in one corner and meeting the above conditions.

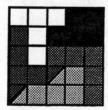

Another solution is to cut an I out of the middle of the cake in the following manner:

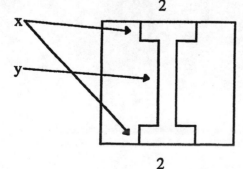

A generalized solution for the cake above is that for the segments denoted as x and y the following relationship exists: y = (5 - 4x)/(5 - 2x) where 5 units is the length of each side. 5 - 2x is the length of the body of the I and 5 - 4x is the total area of the piece minus the area of the two ends. Thus, y(5 - 2x) = 5 - 4x.

Another solution can be found by making two intersecting I's. An extension that ties this in with measurement is for the students to consider how to cut the cake into five pieces when the cake top is n x n. (Some students will think that these solutions are only valid if the cake top is 5 x 5). Encourage the students to *generalize* their solution to describe how to divide the cake into n pieces.

Chapter 7: Real Numbers: Rationals & Irrationals

Chapter Overview:

As technology (especially calculators) becomes more and more prevalent for everyday use, as well as for scientific purposes, so does the use of decimals (and percent). At the same time, ratio and proportion are also quite useful to solve a variety of real-world problems. In this chapter you will explore problems involving decimal, percent, ratio and proportion. Furthermore, to deepen your understanding of rational numbers (which is what the foregoing kinds of numbers are!), you will study the properties of rational numbers and be introduced to still another kind of number, the irrational numbers.

Big Mathematical Ideas:

problem-solving strategies, conjecturing, verifying, decomposing, generalizing, representation, using language & symbolism, limit, mathematical structure

NCTM Standards Links:

K- 4 : Mathematics as problem solving; Mathematics as communication; Mathematics as reasoning; Mathematical connections; Fractions & decimals

5 - 8: Mathematics as problem solving; Mathematics as communication; Mathematics as reasoning; Mathematical connections; Number & number relationships

Chapter Outline:

Notes 7.1—Exploring Ratio and Proportion Ideas

MATH CONTENT

- Ratios, equivalent ratios, proportions

CONNECTIONS

- Exercises and More Problems: #41

TIMETABLE

- 10 minutes for activity
- 10 minutes for class discussion

ACTIVITY DISCUSSION

During the discussion of the activity, ask each group to give their definition of proportion. Then come to a consensus on which definition is most meaningful [conventional definition—two ratios that are equal form a proportion]. Ask the students for strategies to use in solving a proportion for a missing term. The phrase "cross multiply" is likely to be given so ask what is the meaning behind the technique of cross multiplication. Why does cross multiplying work? [cross multiplying is multiplying by LCM of denominators to eliminate the fractions].

ACTIVITY SOLUTIONS

1. a. 15 : 10
   b. 3 : 2
   c. 10 : 15
   d. 2 : 3
2. 15 women; students may have a number of ways to find this answer
3. answers may vary; conventional definition is that two ratios that are equal form a proportion

Notes 7.2—Solving Problems using Proportions

MATH CONTENT

- Ratios, equivalent ratios, proportions

TIMETABLE

- 10-15 minutes for activity
- 5 minutes for class discussion

ACTIVITY DISCUSSION
Have students share their strategies for arriving at solutions.

ACTIVITY SOLUTIONS
1. 30 runs
2. 1/2 meter or 50 centimeters
3. 6 cm
4. 32
5. $500

Notes 7.3—Graphing Proportion Problems

MATH CONTENT

- Ratios, equivalent ratios, proportions

TIMETABLE

- 10-15 minutes for activity
- 5 minutes for class discussion

ACTIVITY DISCUSSION
After the students have finished, have different groups give their solutions and justify their graphs. Discuss which graphs should depict continuous lines and which should consist of integral ordered pairs.

ACTIVITY SOLUTIONS
Note: Most of these can be represented with either variable as the independent variable. The exceptions are the model locomotive and the taxes.
1. $j = (2/3) a$; not a continuous graph
2. $m = (1/24) o$; continuous graph
3. $d = (3/4) a$; continuous graph
4. $y = (8/3) x$; continuous graph
5. $t = (800/40000)p$; continuous graph

Notes 7.4—Introducing Decimal Representation

MATH CONTENT

- Decimal representation of rational numbers

MATERIALS

- Base ten blocks (1 cube, 9 flats, 9 longs, 9 units per group)

TIMETABLE

- 15 minutes for activity
- 10 minutes for class discussion

ACTIVITY DISCUSSION

During the discussion, ask how decimals fit into the idea of rational numbers. [Are decimals rational numbers? How do they fit the definition of rational number?] Point out that fractional representation and decimal representation are two ways to write rational numbers. Ask different groups to share their pictures for modeling operations with decimals. Have them justify the regrouping process they must use.

ACTIVITY SOLUTIONS

1. answers will vary; one possibility is 3/4 and .75
2. change the fraction into a decimal or change the decimal into a fraction and compare
3. with strip of paper, fold into fifths and cover two sections; with base ten blocks, select 2 out of every 5 units
4. a. illustration should show 2 cubes, 3 flats, 4 longs and 6 units being combined with 1 cube, 2 flats, and 7 longs; start combining the units and work up through larger blocks; regroup as needed; final representation should show 3 cubes, 6 flats, 1 long and 6 units (3.616)
   b. illustration should show 3 cubes and 3 flats; trade in 1 flat for 10 longs, then trade in 1 long for 10 units; take away 5 units, 7 longs; then trade in 1 cube for 10 flats, take away 8 flats and determine what is left; final representation should show 4 flats, 2 longs and 5 units (.425)
   c. illustration should show 2 cubes, 3 flats and 5 longs; then add another set of the same blocks (2 cubes, 3 flats and 5 longs) and regroup as needed; final representation should show 4 cubes and 7 flats (4.7)
   d. illustration should show 4 cubes, 8 flats and 4 longs; separate these into 4 equal groups and determine how many is in each group; final representation should show 1 cube, 2 flats and 1 long (1.21)

Notes 7.5—Explaining Decimal Point Placement

MATH CONTENT

- Decimal point placement rules with operations

TIMETABLE

- 15 minutes for activity
- 10 minutes for class discussion

ACTIVITY DISCUSSION

For the decimal point placement rules the students' verification may center on specific examples. Try to get them to generalize their explanations.

ACTIVITY SOLUTIONS

Some possible generalizations are as follows:

Addition and subtraction—the digits in like powers of ten positions must be added together or subtracted from each other which is equivalent to lining up the decimal points [if written in expanded form it is clear that like terms can be grouped together to be added or subtracted]

Multiplication—the product of negative powers of ten will be ten to the sum of the powers which is equivalent to counting the number of decimal places in both factors

Division—$a/b = a/b \times 1 = a/b \times c/c$, where c is not 0, explains why the multiplication can be done; the actual placement of the decimal point, then, is an application of the distributive property [$a.b/c = a/c + (b/10^n)/c$].

Notes 7.6—Modeling Operations with Decimals

MATH CONTENT

- Multiplication and division of decimals

MATERIALS

- Base ten blocks (1 cube, 9 flats, 9 longs, 9 units per group)

TIMETABLE

- 20 minutes for activity
- 15 minutes for class discussion

ACTIVITY DISCUSSION

For each of the situations in Activity 7.6, groups should choose which block or blocks represent 1. Do one example with the class first before they begin working in their groups. [Example: 1/2 • 1/3—start with three longs, take one of the three, then take 5 units on the long (three longs = 1)]

Students may confuse #4 and #6 and think they are the same situation. Discuss the difference in the action taking place. For #4, the idea is to see how many groups of .2 are contained in .6. In #6, the idea is to see how many groups of .6 are contained in .2.

Have different groups share their modeling of the operations. Discuss how the idea of multiple representations is present in this activity.

ACTIVITY SOLUTIONS

Some ways of modeling these operations are shown below.

#1—start with nine longs and six units, separate into three groups (3 longs and 2 units—sharing) or separate into groups of three longs (3 and 1/5 groups or 3.2—repeated subtraction) [one long = 1]

#2—start with three longs, take one of the three, then take 2 units on the long [three longs = 1]

#3—start with one flat, take half (50 units on the flat), then take half of the 50 units (25 units) [one flat = 1]

#4—start with six longs, separate into 2 groups (3 longs—sharing) or into groups of two longs (3 groups—repeated subtraction) [one flat = 1]

#5—start with seven longs, separate into 3 groups (2 and 1/3 longs—sharing) or separate into groups of 3 longs (2 and 1/3 groups—repeated subtraction) [one flat = 1]

#6—start with one flat, take .2 of the flat (20 units on the flat), have 1/3 of a group of 60 units [one flat = 1]

#7—start with 12 longs, take one fourth of the longs (3), then take 2/3 of the three longs (2 longs out of 12 = 2/12 or 1/6) [12 longs = 1]

#8—start with one flat, take .4 of the flat (40 units), then take 1.25 of the 40 units (50 units) [one flat = 1]

Notes 7.7—Converting Decimals to Fractions

MATH CONTENT

- Conversion of fractions to decimals and decimals to fractions, terminating, non-terminating and irrational decimals

CONNECTIONS

- Exercises and More Problems: #42-45

TIMETABLE

- 30 minutes for activity
- 15 minutes for class discussion

ACTIVITY DISCUSSION

Changing repeating decimals into fractions (#7 and #8) will be difficult for the students. You might suggest to the students to think about the terminating decimals that are bounds for the repeating decimals. For example, for #7b 4.45 and 4.46 are bounds for the repeating decimal. Then thinking of these terminating decimals and their fractional expressions may help the students in converting the repeating decimals to fractions. The main point is to tie this to rational numbers, and distinguishing between rational and irrational numbers.

During the discussion of this activity, guide the students in seeing what is the essential point in determining whether a fraction is terminating or non-terminating [in simplest form, the prime factorization of the denominator can have only powers of 2 and 5]. Have different groups share their *generalizations* of the processes for converting terminating and non-terminating decimals into fractions. Discuss the idea of irrational numbers and where they fit in the total picture of the sets of numbers that we have discussed.

ACTIVITY SOLUTIONS

1. .5, .$\overline{3}$, .25, .2, .1$\overline{6}$, .$\overline{142857}$, .125, .$\overline{1}$, .1
2/3. they can be categorized as terminating or non-terminating, repeating
4. the terminating decimals have fraction representations that have only factors of 2 and/or 5 in the denominator, which means that they can be written as fractions with denominators that are powers of 10
5. a. 345/1000   b. 412/100   c. -12359/10000
6. take the number, without decimal point, and place it over the power of ten that corresponds to how many decimal places it has

7. a. let x = .3333 . . ., then 10x = 3.3333 . . ., then subtracting the first equation from the second equation yields 9x = 3, so x = 1/3
    b. let x = 4.454545 . . ., then 100x = 445.4545 . . ., then subtracting the first equation from the second equation yields 99x = 441, so x = 99/441 = 11/49
    c. let x = 1.0323232 . . ., then 100x = 103.232323 . . ., then subtracting the first equation from the second equation yields 99x = 102.2 which is 990x = 1022 and so x = 1022/990 = 511/495
8. set the repeating decimal equal to x, then multiply both sides of this equation by the power of ten that corresponds to the number of digits in the block of repeating digits; subtract the first equation from the second equation and then solve for x; the idea is to get rid of the repeating decimal block
9. no, these cannot be converted to fractions

10. non-terminating, non-repeating decimals; these are irrational numbers
11. 4
12. 4
13. 1
14. 11 and 12 involve modular arithmetic ideas; 13 involves a pattern

Notes 7.8—Introducing Percent Representation

MATH CONTENT

- Percents, percent representation of fractions

CONNECTIONS

- Exercises and More Problems: #39-40

TIMETABLE

- 20 minutes for activity
- 10 minutes for class discussion

ACTIVITY DISCUSSION
Have different groups share and justify their solutions and method of solving.

ACTIVITY SOLUTIONS
1. $60 - 1/4(60) - 30 - .10(60) = \$9$
2. $240 - 24 + 24 + 48 - .25(48) - .50(48) = \$252$
3. he bought one for $500 and made 20% on it ($100); he bought one for $750 and lost 20% on it ($150); his total expenses were $1250 and his income was $1200 so he lost $50 on the deal
4. let x = smallest set, y = middle set, z = largest set; then $y = 2x$ and $z = 3y$; so x, $2x$, and $6x$ represent the sets for a total of $9x$; thus, the smallest is 1/9 or approximately 11% of the total, the middle is 2/9 or approximately 22% of the total, and the largest is 6/9 or approximately 67% of the total.

Notes 7.9—Pay Those Taxes: A Game of Percents and Primes

MATH CONTENT

- Percents, prime numbers

MATERIALS

- Spinners (two per group), cards with the numbers 2, 3, 5, 7, 11 for each group

TIMETABLE

- 25 minutes for activity
- 5 minutes for class discussion

ACTIVITY DISCUSSION

You may want to have a group discussion and play a bit of the game in order to have all students understand the rules of the game. The important point for discussion following the playing of the game is the strategies involved in playing the game—which two-digit number to choose, when to buy a prime number, why buy a prime number, which prime number(s) to buy.

Notes 7.10—Comparing Fractions, Decimals and Percents

MATH CONTENT

- Fractions, decimals, percents

CONNECTIONS

- Exercises and More Problems: #47

TIMETABLE

- 15 minutes for activity
- 5 minutes for class discussion

ACTIVITY DISCUSSION

Ask students to share their strategies for determining the one that does not belong. Note: The percent change problems may be difficult for students.

ACTIVITY SOLUTIONS

1. C
2. D
3. D
4. B
5. C
6. A
7. C
8. D
9. answers will vary; some possibilities are: 5 : 50; 2 : 20; 3 : 30

Notes 7.11—Four in a Row: A Game of Decimals and Factors

MATH CONTENT

- Decimals, factors, multiplication of decimals

TIMETABLE

- 15 minutes for activity
- 5 minutes for class discussion

ACTIVITY DISCUSSION
Have students discuss what mathematical ideas are used in this game after playing it.

Notes 7.12—Exploring Circles: Approximating an Irrational Number

MATH CONTENT

- Pi, irrational numbers

MATERIALS

- Cuisenaire rods

TIMETABLE

- 25 minutes for activity
- 10 minutes for class discussion

ACTIVITY DISCUSSION

In this activity, students are using different Cuisenaire rods for the radius of the circle and then finding circumference and examining the sum, difference, product and ratio of the circumference and the diameter. It is important to have students fill in the table (#2) for the circle that has the radius the length of the red rod. THEN have the students complete #3; have them think about and make a prediction for what will happen as the size of the rod and the circle increases.

Some groups might place the white rods (1 cm) inside the circle to approximate the circumference. Some groups will place white rods around the outside of the circles. Some many even alternate the rods, by placing one inside and the next outside. This is a good point for discussion—what is a good approximation? How could it be better? Discuss the idea of limit and how by using larger rods for the radius and forming the polygons with the unit rods, the polygons are approaching the shape of the circle.

ACTIVITY SOLUTIONS

1. a. 4 cm   b. around 24 cm; see discussion above
6. students should find that C, D, C+D, C-D, C•D all increase but C÷D remains fairly constant
7. pi (π)

Notes 7.13—Constructing Irrational Numbers

MATH CONTENT

- Constructing irrational numbers

CONNECTIONS

- Exercises and More Problems: #46

TIMETABLE

- 15 minutes for activity
- 5 minutes for class discussion

ACTIVITY DISCUSSION

You may need to suggest to students to think about using right triangles and the Pythagorean Theorem to help them in constructing these segments.

ACTIVITY SOLUTIONS

1. construct a right triangle with legs of 1 in and 1 in, then the hypotenuse will be $\sqrt{2}$ inches long
2. construct a right triangle with legs of 2 in and 3 in, then the hypotenuse will be $\sqrt{13}$ inches long
3. construct a right triangle with legs of 1 in and 1 in, then the hypotenuse will be $\sqrt{2}$ inches long; construct a right triangle with legs of 1 in and 2 in, then the hypotenuse will be $\sqrt{5}$ inches long; construct a right triangle with legs of $\sqrt{2}$ in and $\sqrt{5}$ in, then the hypotenuse will be $\sqrt{7}$ inches long
4. described in #1-3

Notes 7.14—Properties of Rational and Irrational Numbers

MATH CONTENT

- Rational numbers, irrational numbers, group properties

CONNECTIONS

- Exercises and More Problems: #48

TIMETABLE

- 20 minutes for activity
- 10 minutes for class discussion

ACTIVITY DISCUSSION

Discuss closure of the set of whole numbers for subtraction and division [not closed under subtraction—leads to set of integers; not closed under division—leads to set of rational numbers]. Ask the students for their definition of a rational number. [any number that can be represented by a/b where a and b are integers and b ≠ 0]. Ask the students to explain why b is not 0, why a and b are integers, why sometimes a/b is a whole number, sometimes a/b is an integer and sometimes a/b is a rational number that is not a whole number or an integer. Ask the students to describe the relationships among the set of rational numbers, the set of whole numbers, and the set of integers. This would be a good time to generate a Venn diagram illustrating the relationships among these sets of numbers.

When discussing the group properties, talk about them in relation to the set of rational numbers, as well as natural numbers, whole numbers, integers, and irrational numbers. Discuss the mathematical structure of the set of real numbers. Have the students verify which properties are valid for which set of numbers. Wrap up the ideas about the mathematical structure and discuss the relationships among all the sets of numbers we have examined.

ACTIVITY SOLUTIONS

1. a. True. Adding two rational numbers always results in a rational number.
   b. True. The product of any two rational numbers is always a rational number.
   c. True. Order in which two rational numbers are added doesn't matter.
   d. True. Order in which two rational numbers are multiplied doesn't matter.
   e. True. The grouping of rational numbers when added doesn't affect the sum.
   f. True. The grouping of rational numbers when multiplied doesn't affect the sum.
   g. True. The rational number $0/p$, where p is any integer except 0, is the identity for addition.
   h. True. The rational number $1/1 = 1$ is the identity for multiplication.
   i. True. If p/q is a rational number, there is a unique additive inverse, $-p/q$.
      True. If p/q is a rational number, there is a unique multiplicative inverse, q/p, if p is not 0.
2. All of the properties in #1 are valid for irrational numbers also except for 1.a. and 1.b. The irrational numbers are not closed under addition or multiplication. For example, $\sqrt{2} + -\sqrt{2} = 0$, which shows that the sum of two irrational numbers is not necessarily irrational. Similarly, $\sqrt{2} \times (1/\sqrt{2}) = 1$, so irrational number are not closed under multiplication.
3. All of the properties in #1 are valid for the set of real numbers. The two that did not hold for the set of irrational numbers (see #2), now hold because the irrational numbers are combined with the rational numbers.

4.   Let R = set of real numbers, Q = set of rational numbers, I = set of irrational numbers, Z = set of integers, W = set of whole numbers, and N = set of natural numbers (also called counting numbers). Then the following relationships exist among these sets:

Q and I are both subsets of R and Q and I are disjoint.
N is a subset of W, which is a subset of Z, which is a subset of Q.

Chapter 8: Patterns & Functions

Chapter Overview:

The concept of function is a central theme, a big idea, running through many areas of mathematics. In this chapter, the idea of function, which is a particular kind of relationship between to or more sets of objects, is introduced through explorations of patterns. Also emphasized will be different ways to represent functional relationships.

Big Mathematical Ideas:

> problem-solving strategies, functions & relations, representation, conjecturing, verifying, mathematical structure

NCTM Standards Links:

> *K - 4:* Mathematics as problem solving; Mathematics as communication; Mathematics as reasoning; Mathematical connections; Patterns & relationships

> *5 - 8:* Mathematics as problem solving; Mathematics as communication; Mathematics as reasoning; Mathematical connections; Patterns & functions

Chapter Outline:

Notes 8.1—Exploring Variables

MATH CONTENT

- Variables, relationships among variables

MATERIALS

- Graph paper (as an alternative to using the supplied grid)

CONNECTIONS

- Exercises and More Problems: #1-11, 49

TIMETABLE

- 20 minutes for activity
- 10 minutes for class discussion

ACTIVITY DISCUSSION

Students will likely have some familiarity with data represented as tables, as graphs, and with function (or functional) notation. Many of the activities throughout Chapter 8 will involve students' interpreting and thinking critically about these representations. Thus, the activities of this section provide a foundation for the remaining activities in the chapter.

As students work with the data in tables, you may urge them to consider the advantages and disadvantages to such a representation. For example, the table does not reveal what happened to the temperature *between* the recorded times. You might ask the following questions:

- Using only the table, is it possible to determine if the temperature was ever exactly 18°?
- Is it possible to determine *when* the temperature was 18°?
- How could the table have been made more helpful?

Although a grid is provided for students to plot the graph, you may wish to either provide graph paper, or encourage students to bring their own. For many of the graphing activities throughout this chapter, grids are not provided. Also, you may wish to encourage students to use spreadsheet software or graphing calculators for plotting data.

As with the tables, urge your students to consider the advantages and disadvantages of using graphs to represent data. For example, the graph provides a way to quickly spot trends (increases or decreases). You might ask the following questions:

- What kinds of questions are easier to answer by looking at a graph than by looking at a table?
- What kinds of questions are *harder* to answer by looking at a graph than by looking at a table?
- What are some factors to consider in making a graph make sense to others?
- When looking at graphs in the media, what are some common features you notice?

When using function notation, it is important to inform others as to the meaning of the symbols you choose. We have introduced function notation *without* explaining the meaning of the symbols. It is important, therefore, to establish in advance just what the symbols mean. For example, does T(10) = 11 mean "The temperature at 10 a.m. was 11¡ F," or, "The temperature hit 10¡ F at 11 a.m.?"

ACTIVITY SOLUTIONS

1. a. 29°F b.   8 a.m.
2. a. Between 2 p.m. and 6 p.m. the temperature dropped 23 degrees. Between 2 p.m. and 4 p.m. the decrease in temperature was 13 degrees which is 10 degrees less than between 2 p.m. and 6 p.m.
    b. The increase in temperature between 6 a.m. and noon was 20 degrees.
3. From 3 p.m. to 11 p.m. the temperature decreased from 27° F to 0° F due to the sun going down.
4.

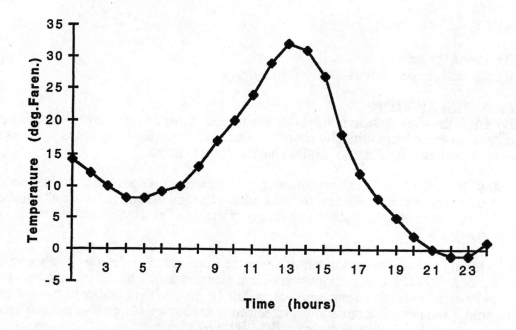

Time (hours)

5. a. At 1 p.m. the temperature was the highest: 32° F.
    b. At 10 p.m. and 11 p.m. the temperature was the lowest: -1° F.
6. a. T(7) = 10, (7,10). At 7 a.m. the temperature was 10° F.
    b. T(19) = 5, (19,5). At 7 p.m. the temperature was 5° F.
    c. T(21) = 0, (21, 0). At 9 p.m. temperature was 0° F.
    d. T(12) = 29, (12,29). At noon the temperature was 29° F.
7. The temperature is affected by such factors as the position of the sun in the sky, the season, the humidity, and the wind. The temperature cools at night and starts rising as the sun comes up. Reaches the highest pick around midday and then starts cooling off as the sun goes down.

Notes 8.2—Investigating Variables Through Data in Tables

MATH CONTENT

- Variables, relationships among variables

MATERIALS

- Graph paper

CONNECTIONS

- Exercises and More Problems: #14, 37, 50
- Some of the questions in Activity 8.2 challenge students to look for a way to maximize profit. In Activity 8.8, students will explore such optimizations in more depth

TIMETABLE

- 20 minutes for activity
- 10 minutes for class discussion

ACTIVITY DISCUSSION

Like Activity 8.1, the activity here involves data in tables. However, the activities in this section require students to think more critically about the data. For example, #4 requires students to extend the table and, having done so, explore the resulting patterns.

Questions 4, 8, 10, and 11 deal with optimization. While many may associate optimization with calculus, we do not do so here. Rather, students are challenged to look for a "best" solution (in this case, a maximum profit), by exploring patterns in a table. Students will explore this idea further in Activity 8.8.

When students deal with functional notation, stress the importance of *defining* one's variables. For example, $B(1.90)=100$ is meaningless until one explains what each of the numbers means. Better would be an introductory sentence such as, "$B(\$x)$ means 'the number of bags of popcorn that will be sold if the price is x dollars.'" Furthermore, encourage students to include units in their notation, so that $B(1.90)=100$ becomes $B(\$1.90)=100$ *bags*.

ACTIVITY SOLUTIONS

1. The more expensive popcorn is, the lesser the amount that will be sold by the theater.
2. Reasonable. More people would buy a bag of popcorn if it is cheap.
3. Yes, it is possible to calculate the optimal price.
4.

cost ($)	# of bags sold during movie	profit ($)
1.90	100	65.00
1.95	95	66.50
2.00	90	67.50
2.05	85	68.00
2.10	80	68.00
2.15	75	67.50

From the table it is clear that a price of either $2.05 or $2.10 per bag of popcorn will generate the maximum profit.

5. a. B(1.90) = 100   b. B(2.15) = 75
6. B(2.40) = 50
7. When the theater sells popcorn for $1.90 per bag, the profit is $65.00.
8. P(2.10) = 68
9. Size of the bag and taste of the popcorn are two influential factors.
10. The sales go down (less popcorn is sold, less profit is made.)
11. More bags of popcorn are sold but the profit goes down. For example, if the theater sells popcorn for $1.25 per bag, the profit will be zero.

Notes 8.3—Investigating Variables Through Data in Graphs

MATH CONTENT

- Variables, relationships among variables

MATERIALS

- Graph paper

CONNECTIONS

- Exercises and More Problems: #30-32, 46, 51

TIMETABLE

- 20 minutes for activity
- 10 minutes for class discussion

ACTIVITY DISCUSSION

Question 5 gets at the idea of a *continuous* function: a function that changes "smoothly," rather than in discrete steps. The temperature, for example, cannot change from 60° to 70° without being 62° at some time. Similarly, if you travel 45 miles per hour for part of a trip, and 50 miles per hour for part of that trip, then there must have been a time when you were traveling 49 miles per hour. In calculus, this concept is addressed more formally, as the "Intermediate Value Theorem." Here, however, it is enough for students to recognize situations in which "You can't get from point A to point B without getting to all the points in between."

In questions 6 and 7, you might want to discuss the differences between "change" and "rate of change." In later activities, when students explore the concept of slope, such distinctions will be very important. Consider such questions as:

- When might you be more interested in finding the change than in finding the rate of change?
- When might you be more interested in finding the rate of change than in finding the change?
- Is the "steepness" of a graph related more closely to change, or to rate of change?

ACTIVITY SOLUTIONS

1. A line plot is better than a bar graph because it allows you to see the change in the temperature more clearly.
2. At 4 p.m. the temperature was 88° F.
3. At 6 a.m. and 6 p.m. the temperature was in the 60s.
4. At midnight, 2 and 4 a.m.
5. Yes. Between 8 and 10 a.m. the temperature increased from 70¡ F to 85¡ F, which means that the temperature had to be 73¡ at some time during that interval.
6. The change was 8 degrees in two hours.
7. Therefore, the rate of change was 4 degrees in one hour.
8. It might have been somewhere between 61¡ and 70°, but there is no way to know for certain.
9. Between 4 and 6 a.m.
10. Between 4 and 6 p.m.
11. The temperature is increasing most rapidly when the slope of the line is graph becomes the steepest.

12. Various phenomena might have contributed to the drop from 4 to 6 p.m. For example, the sun was beginning to go down during that period, but there might also have been a thunderstorm.

13. No, the data are not sufficient. The maximum temperature might have occurred sometime between noon and 2 p.m. then dropped back to 96° by 2 p.m.

Notes 8.4—Interpreting Graphs

MATH CONTENT

- Variables, relationships among variables, graphs

CONNECTIONS

- Exercises and More Problems: #12-13, 34-36

TIMETABLE

- 15 minutes for activity
- 5 minutes for class discussion

ACTIVITY DISCUSSION

One feature that all of the graphs in this activity have in common is that none of them contain any numbers. Often it is important for people to be able to notice non-numeric features of graphs. For example, in a graph of selling price versus profit, we might be interested in questions such as "What happens to profit as the selling price increases?" or "Does a big change in selling price result in a big change in profits?"

The purpose of these activities is to engage students in such reasoning. For example, in problem 2 of "Identifying Graphs of Functions," each of the graphs shows the temperature increasing until the middle of the year, then decreasing until the end of the year. But each of the graphs shows this increase occurring in very different ways. You might consider asking such questions as:

- What could you say about the temperature each month if the graph really were a straight line?
- How would a similar graph for Southern California (or another city) differ from the Chicago graph?
- Are there cities that would have a graph that looks just like Chicago, but shifted slightly upward (or downward)?
- Are there cities that would have a graph that looks just like Chicago, but "flipped upside down?"
- Suppose the headline of a Chicago newspaper was, "Harsh Winter Ahead!" How would you expect the temperature graph to change?

You could also encourage students to write their own such questions about the various graphs in these activities.

ACTIVITY SOLUTIONS

1. a. Graph 1 is wrong since the sales should go down, not up, as the price of the house increases. Graph 2 is the correct one. Graph 3 is wrong since the sales cannot be negative.
    b. Location, size of the house, advertisement and average income of potential buyers are among many factors that can affect the sale of a house.

c.

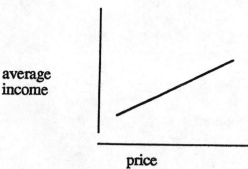

average
income

price

Identifying Graphs of Functions

1. a. Graph *c*
    b. Graph *a* might represent a bathtub filling and then emptying as soon as it is full.
    c. Graph *b* might represent a bathtub emptying for a time and then beginning to fill again and then filling much more rapidly before being emptied quickly.
2. a. Graph *c*
    b.
    c.
3. a. Graph *b*
    b.
    c.
4. a. Graph *c*
    b.
    c.

Notes 8.5—Investigating and Describing Numerical Patterns

MATH CONTENT

- Variables, relationships among variables, graphs

MATERIALS

- Graphing calculator for plotting data from tables (optional)

CONNECTIONS

- Exercises and More Problems: #26-29, 38, 48

TIMETABLE

- 20 minutes for activity
- 10 minutes for class discussion

ACTIVITY DISCUSSION

A common way that functions are often informally introduced at the elementary level are through "Guess my rule" activities. In these activities, at teacher or student is the "rule maker" who decides on a rule that converts an input number to an output number. For example, the rule maker's rule might be "square the number and subtract three." The rule maker's job is to make others guess the rule by giving examples of the rule. Here, for instance, the rule maker might say, "If 3 goes in, 6 comes out." Of course, one such example is not sufficient to guess the rule. So, the rule maker gives one example at a time, or answers questions from others such as, "What happens if a 10 goes in?" The object for the other students is to guess the rule with as few examples as possible.

Students should be encouraged to describe rules both in words, and with variables. "Square the input number and subtract three to get the output number" is a good way to describe the rule in words. Using variables, we might say, "If the input is n, the output is $n^2 - 3$."

In a number table, students will often be tempted to look for a pattern going *down* the "Output" column. For example, in the first table, students might say, "Each output number is three more than the previous output number." A rule that is based on knowing the *previous* value is called a "recursive rule." While valuable in describing patterns, such a rule is not very helpful if one wants to know the 300th number in the table, because the 300th number depends on first knowing the 299th number, which requires knowing the 298th number, and so on. Do not discourage such recursive rules. Instead, stress the importance of using recursive rules along with "explicit rules" (such as the above $n^2 - 3$), which relates the input number to the output number.

ACTIVITY SOLUTIONS

1.

Input	Output
1	3
2	6
3	9
4	12
5	15
6	18
17	51

a. If you divide the output by the input you always get 3.
b. If the input were x, the output would be 3x.
c. If the output were n, the input would be n/3.

2.

Input	Output
1	19
2	18
3	17
4	16
10	10
13.5	6.5
0	20

a. As the input increases by one, the output decreases by one. The input and output always add up to 20.
b. If the input were h, output would be 20-h.
c. If the output were j, the input would be 20-j.

3.

Input	Output
1	1
6	11
20	39
13	25
5	9
21	41
11.5	22

a. The current output is equal to twice the current input minus 1.
b. If the input were z, the output would be 2z - 1.
c. If the output were d, the input must be (d + 1)/2.

4.

Input	Output
3	12
7	56
1	2
0	0
25	650
26	702
47	2256

a. The current output is equal to a product of the current input and one more than the current input.
b. If the input were x, the output would be x(x + 1).
c. If the output were y, the input will be $-1/2 + (1+4y)^{1/2}$.

5. There are numerous acceptable answers for this. One possible table and rule would be the following:

Input	Output
1	3
2	5
3	7
4	9
5	11
6	13
7	15

If the input were n, the output would be $2n + 1$.

Notes 8.6—Investigating Numerical Situations

MATH CONTENT

- Relationships among variables

MATERIALS

- Graphing calculator for plotting data from tables (optional)

CONNECTIONS

- Exercises and More Problems: #52

TIMETABLE

- 15 minutes for activity
- 5-10 minutes for class discussion

ACTIVITY DISCUSSION

This activity takes the rule making of Activity 8.5 and applies it to a realistic situation: that of scheduling a tournament. The problem leads naturally to creating a table and looking for patterns. Once again, students may be tempted to settle for recursive rules. Encourage them, however, to additionally find an explicit rule.

ACTIVITY SOLUTIONS

1. Solutions will vary depending on the number of teams you choose. As an example, look at the table below:

number of teams	number of games
2	1
3	2
4	6
5	10
6	15
7	21
8	28

2.

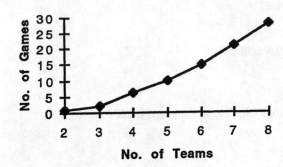

3. It doesn't make sense to connect the points since the relationship between the number of games and the number of teams is discrete (it is not possible, for example, to play half a game in the tournament, or use half a team.). The more teams involved, the more games will be played. But the rate of change is not constant; in fact, the number of games seems to grow faster than the number of teams.

4. By connecting the data points you should get a sense for the trend in the direction the data are going, thereby making it easier to predict where other data points should be. So, for 9 teams, there should be about 35 or 36 games played.

5. The general formula for the n teams is: number of games = $n(n-1) \div 2$

6. $n(n-1)/2 = 120$;
    $n^2 - n - 240 = 0$;
    Factor: $(n - 16)(n + 15) = 0$;

    $n = 16$ or $n = 15$.

    The smaller number being impossible, we get the answer: 16 teams

Notes 8.7—Identifying Rules and Functions

MATH CONTENT

- Relationships among variables, functions

MATERIALS

- Graphing calculator for plotting data from tables (optional)
- Graph paper

CONNECTIONS

- Exercises and More Problems: #19-25, 39-45, 47

TIMETABLE

- 20 minutes for activity
- 10 minutes for class discussion

ACTIVITY DISCUSSION

In many ways, Activity 8.7 can be thought of as the heart of the "Patterns and Functions" chapter. The major idea of this section is pattern generalization and description. While Activities 8.1 through 8.6 encouraged looking at patterns and interpreting their various features, Activity 8.7 focuses on *finding and describing* such patterns. Activity 8.7 also provides a foundation on which Activities 8.8 (optimization) and 8.9 - 8.11 (iteration) build.

Often, students are used to memorizing rules and formulas (such as the Pythagorean Theorem and the formula for the area of a circle). Activity 8.7 suggests that mathematics is not *using* rules as much as it is *finding* rules. When do we use rules? Often, we will use rules if we plan to make the same type of calculation over and over again. For example, we may not use a rule to determine how much money we will have in our savings account next year, but if we would also like to make similar calculations for 10, 20, and 30 years from now, it will be very helpful to find a rule that explains how to calculate the balance given the number of years. Similarly, a formula for the area of a rectangle may not be very necessary to find the area of *one* rectangle. But, for a carpet layer, who may make such calculations routinely, a formula may be essential.

So, Activity 8.7 has two goals: *finding* rules and *using* those rules. There is no surefire way of finding rules to describe patterns. You will likely find that some students are better than others at finding rules. To help those who have trouble generalizing patterns, encourage the more successful students to describe how they "discovered" their rules. What patterns did they notice? Which ideas worked? Which ideas failed? How did you know when you were on the right track? Such discussions can only help those students who may struggle to make sense of numerical patterns. You may even encourage all students to write and discuss how they answer, "What is the best advice you can give to people on how to discover numerical patterns?"

As for *using* the discovered rules, you could ask students, once they know a rule, to write as many different kinds of questions as they can think of that can be answered using the discovered rule. This may lead not only to a better understanding of mathematical rules, but to a deeper appreciation of the usefulness of such rules.

ACTIVITY SOLUTIONS

1. a.

Time (min)	Distance (km)
10	12.5
20	25
40	50
50	62.5
60	75
80	100
120	150

b. If you know the number of minutes, you can multiply by 1.25 to find the number of kilometers. $d = 1.25t$ (where d is distance in kilometers, and t is time in minutes)

c. Speed of the car is $500 \cdot 2.5 = 1.25$ km/min

d. $d = 1.25 \cdot 20$ km. In 20 min the distance will be 25 km.

e.

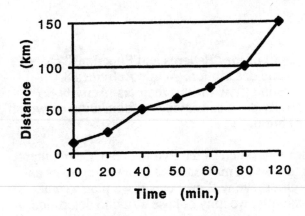

2. a.

No. of subscr. sold	weekly pay (dollars)
1	115
2	130
3	145
6	190
10	250
12	280
15	325

b. $P = 100 + 15 \cdot S$; $S = (P - 100)/15$

c. i. $P = 100 + 15 \times 9 = 235$

   ii. $P = 100 + 0 = 100$

   iii. $S = (400 - 100) / 15 = 20$

Notes 8.8—Looking for an Optimal Solution

MATH CONTENT

- Optimization

MATERIALS

- Graphing calculator for plotting data from tables (optional)
- Graph paper

CONNECTIONS

- Exercises and More Problems: #15-18, 53

TIMETABLE

- 30-40 minutes for activity
- 15 minutes for class discussion

ACTIVITY DISCUSSION

How can we maximize our profit? How can we use the materials we have to construct the biggest box? How can we minimize the likelihood of making an error? Often, we are not only interested in finding *a* solution. Sometimes, when there are many possible solutions, we are interested in finding the best or *optimal* solution.

The purpose of Activity 8.8 is for students to use the table- and rule-making of Activity 8.7 to look for patterns. Here are some things to encourage as students work on Activity 8.8:

- Know your constraints. For example, in making a paper box, there is a limit on how large a square may be cut from each corner. Knowing this limit can make the search for a solution easier.
- Be systematic. The first couple guesses may be "wild," but each subsequent guess should be chosen in a way that will (hopefully) improve on previous guesses. Ask students to justify their choices of guesses.
- Don't always assume that there is an answer. For example, if you were asked to "Find two numbers whose sum is 10 and whose product is as small as possible," you will find that there is no minimum product.

Looking for minimal or maximal solutions is a common activity in calculus. Some more experienced students may recall how to solve some of the problems in Activity 8.8 by using calculus. While this should certainly not be discouraged, you should:

- Encourage students to find alternate approaches to the problem. Some problems, such as numbers 17 and 18 in the "Exercises and More Problems" section of chapter 8 cannot be answered using the typical algorithms of an introductory calculus class.

Encourage students to show, graphically, why the calculus works.

ACTIVITY SOLUTIONS

1. Cutting out one-inch squares:
    V (volume) = $4 \cdot 6 \cdot 2 = 48$ in^3 ; SA (surface area) = $48 + 12 + 16 = 76$ in^2

2. Cutting out two-inch squares: V = $4 \cdot 6 \cdot 2 = 48$ in^3; SA = $24 + 16 + 24 = 64$ in^2

3. Considering only whole numbers, three-inch squares are the largest ones you can cut.
    V = 24 in^3, SA = 44 in^2

4. Considering whole numbers, the maximal *volume* is obtained by cutting out 1- or 2-inch squares from each corner. However, a greater volume is obtained by cutting out squares whose sides are between 1 and 2 inches.

5. Using whole numbers only, maximal surface area is obtained by cutting out 1-inch squares from each corner. Without the whole number constraint, the closer the squares' sides are to 0 inches, the greater the resulting surface area.

6. Cutting out x-inch squares from each corner:
    V = $x(10 - 2x)(8 - 2x)$,   SA = $(10 - 2x)(8 - 2x) + 2x(8 - 2x) + 2x(10 - 2x)$.

7. One way to compare volumes would be to fill each box with rice to see which holds more.

8. Considering only whole numbers, the longest the two congruent sides can be is 59 ft each. However, each side *could* measure 59.9 ft, or 59.9999 ft, etc.

9. Again, considering only whole numbers, the longest the front side can be is 118 ft. But it could be 119.9999999 ft, or any value less than 120 ft.

10. If the pen is square, the area would be $40 \cdot 40 = 1600$ ft^2.

11. A maximum area of 1800 ft^2 is obtained by letting the front side measure 60 feet, and the two congruent sides 30 feet each. Notice that if x is the length of the left and right sides and y is the length of the front side, then $2x + y = 120$. We want to maximize xy, so substituting $y = 120 - 2x$, we get $x(120 - x)$. By trying various values for x, we find that the expression is largest when $x = 30$. (Alternatively, use techniques of calculus).

12. Using whole numbers, the minimum area is 118 ft^2. However, without the whole-number constraint, there is no minimum.

One side of the pen (ft)	Area (ft^2)
1	59
4	224
8	416
10	500
30	900
40	800
59	59

13. Minimum area, assuming whole number lengths is 59 ft^2. Without the whole-number constraint, there is no minimum.

Maximum area is obtained with a 30-foot square pen. The resulting area would be 900 ft^2.

Notes 8.9—Investigating Numerical Functions that Repeat

MATH CONTENT

- Iterating functions

MATERIALS

- Calculator

CONNECTIONS

- Additional problems are embedded in this section. You should pick and choose which of the problems in this activity you wish to complete in class, and which should be assigned for homework.

TIMETABLE

- 20 minutes for activity
- 10 minutes for class discussion

ACTIVITY DISCUSSION

The problems in Activities 8.9 - 8.11 are meant to introduce students to the rich subject of iteration. Recently, computers and graphing calculators have helped to make iteration an important topic. Fractals such as "Mandelbrot's Lake," which are derived from iterated functions, are now easily created on nearly any computer. Calculators make it easy to explore such questions as, "What happens if I start with a number and repeatedly cut it in half?" Iteration also plays an important role in many "everyday" scenarios such as population growth and compounded interest.

There are two key ideas to be highlighted in this section. The first of these ideas is that iteration typically starts with a *seed* and a *rule*. For example, when dealing with compounded interest in a savings account, the "seed" would be the starting amount of money in the account, and the "rule" would be what happens to the money. When dealing with fractals, the seed is typically a simple geometric figure, and the rule explains how to transform a given figure into a new figure. This is best illustrated in Activity 8.11, where the seed is a line segment, and the rule is "Trisect each segment and create an equilateral triangle 'bump' on the middle section."

The other key idea of these activities is that of looking at long range behavior. "What would happen if we were to do this forever?" is a key question that students should begin asking when dealing with iterated functions. For example, in the first activity in this section, students consider, "What happens if I start with a number and repeatedly square it?" The answer, of course, depends on the seed value. When dealing with fractals, realize that the figures drawn are not really fractals. Rather, fractals occur if the iterative process were to "repeat forever."

It is not always easy for students to describe long range behavior. Consider the following three sequences:

$$0, 0.1, 0.2, 0.3, 0.4, 0.5, \ldots$$

$$0, 0.1, 0.3, 0.6, 1.0, 1.5, \ldots$$

$$0, 0.5, 0.75, 0.875, 0.9375, 0.96875, \ldots$$

Students would be correct in stating that in all three sequences, "The numbers keep getting bigger." However, these sequences grow in very different ways. The first increases steadily: each number is 0.1 more than the previous number. In the second sequence, however, each increase is greater than the previous increase. In the third sequence, even though the numbers increase, they do so by smaller and smaller amounts each time. You might give students these three sequences to consider, and ask some of the following questions:

- Will all three sequences eventually go beyond 2.5?
- Which sequence will pass 100 first?
- Is there a certain number that the third sequence will never pass?
- Which sequence "growth rate" most closely resembles the type of growth seen in a savings account?

ACTIVITY SOLUTIONS

1 - 5.   The long-term behavior of squaring depends on the number selected:

Number	Long-Term behavior of squaring
< -1	Grows larger without bound
-1	Sticks at 1
> -1 but < 0	Gets closer and closer to 0
0	Sticks at 0
> 0 but < 1	Gets closer and closer to 0
1	Sticks at 1
> 1	Grows larger without bound

As seen in the table above, squaring numbers does *not* always make them bigger. It is true only for numbers larger than 1 or smaller than –1.

6.   The long-term behavior of *cubing* depends on the number selected:

Number	Long-Term behavior of squaring
< -1	Grows *smaller* without bound
-1	Sticks at -1
> -1 but < 0	Gets closer and closer to 0
0	Sticks at 0
> 0 but < 1	Gets closer and closer to 0
1	Sticks at 1
> 1	Grows larger without bound

More Iteration

1. Beginning with 17, the result will get closer and closer to 4, but will never actually *equal* 4. The same is true regardless of the starting number (unless one starts with 4, which will "stick" at 4 forever).

2. Using the expression $\frac{x}{2}+\frac{1}{x}$: Regardless of the starting number, the values will get closer and closer to 1.414213..., which is equal to the square root of 2.

3. Using the expression $\frac{x}{2}+\frac{a}{x}$: Regardless of the starting number, the values will get closer and closer to the square root of 2a. So, for example, if a were 50, the values would get closer and closer to 10 (which is the square root of 100).

Notes 8.10—Investigating Real-life Iteration: Savings Account Interest

MATH CONTENT

- Iterating functions

MATERIALS

- Calculator

TIMETABLE

- 15 minutes for activity
- 10 minutes for class discussion

ACTIVITY DISCUSSION
See the discussion in Notes 8.9.

ACTIVITY SOLUTIONS

1 - 2.   After one year you will have $100 plus the interest—$6, total being $106.
After the second year your total will be $112.36.

Year	Total after that year ($)
1	106
2	112.36
3	119.102
4	126.25
5	133.82

After 10 years: $179.10. After 20 years: $320.71

3.   General formula: Amount after t years $= 100(1.06)^t$ It will take about 12 years for the money to double.

4.   If the interest rate were 4%, after 10 years, $100 would yield $148.02. At a 4% annual yield, it takes 18 years for your money to double.

5.   There is a way to *approximate* the number of years it takes for your money to double. It's called the "Rule of 72." If the interest rate is x%, then it takes about 72 Ö x years for your money to double. For example, if the interest rate were 3%, it would take about 72 Ö 3 = 24 years for your money to double.

Notes 8.11—Investigating Iteration: Geometry and Fractals

MATH CONTENT

- Iterating functions, fractals

MATERIALS

- Triangular graph paper

TIMETABLE

- 20 minutes for activity
- 10 minutes for class discussion

ACTIVITY DISCUSSION
See the discussion in Notes 8.9.

ACTIVITY SOLUTIONS
2.

Stage	Total length (in "units")
0	1
1	$4/3 \approx 1.33$
2	$16/9 \approx 1.78$
3	$64/27 \approx 2.37$
4	$256/81 \approx 3.16$
5	$1024/243 \approx 4.21$

The length after n stages will be $(4/3)^n$. The first time the length will be greater than 10 units is at stage 9. The first time the length will be greater than 100 units is at stage 17.

Koch's Snowflake
1. Initial perimeter: $27 \cdot 3 = 81$ units. Initial area: $27 \cdot 27 = 729$ triangular units

2.

Stage	Perimeter (Units)	Area (Triangular Units)
1	81	729
2	108	972
3	144	1080
4	192	1128
5	256	1149.333
6	341.333	1158.815

3. At each stage, the perimeter is $(4/3)$ times the perimeter of the previous stage. Thus, the perimeter grows without bound.

4. The area, on the other hand, grows by smaller and smaller amounts. Notice that from stage 1 to stage 2, the area grew by 243, but from stage 5 to stage 6, it grew by less than 10. In the long run, the area will get closer and closer to 1166.4 (notice that it's almost there by stage 6). 1166.4 is exactly 1.6 times the original area. So, it is true that one could draw a circle around the figure and that it would never grow outside of that circle, even though the perimeter grows without bound.

Notes 8.12—Properties of Equations

MATH CONTENT

- Properties of equations

TIMETABLE

- 15 minutes for activity
- 5 minutes for class discussion

ACTIVITY DISCUSSION

This activity could be done as homework or in-class work. The goal here is for the students to think about the mathematical structure that allows us to solve equations for a variable.

ACTIVITY SOLUTIONS

1. $x = 6$ 2. $a = 18$ 3. $w = 5$ 4. $b = -1$

<u>Addition Property of Equality</u>

If a, b, and c are any numbers and $a = b$, then $a + c = b + c$.

(e.g., $x + a = b$ becomes, $x + a - a = b - a$)

<u>Multiplication Property of Equations</u>

If a, b, and c are any numbers and $a = b$, then $a \cdot c = b \cdot c$.

(e.g., if $3x = 15$, then $1/3(3x) = 1/3(15)$)

<u>Substitution Property of Equations</u>

If two expressions are equal to a third expression, they are equal to each other. For example, $2(x+4) = 20$ and $2(x+4) = 2x = 8$, so $2x + 8 = 20$.

Notes 8.13—Using Properties to Solve Equations

MATH CONTENT

- Properties of equations

CONNECTIONS

- Exercises and More Problems: #55

TIMETABLE

- 10 minutes for activity
- 5 minutes for class discussion

ACTIVITY DISCUSSION

This activity could be done as homework or in-class work. The goal here is for the students to think about the mathematical structure that allows us to solve equations for a variable.

ACTIVITY SOLUTIONS

1. $3x + 5 = 2x - 8$
   $3x + 5 - 5 = 2x - 8 - 5$ (addition property of equations)
   $3x = 2x - 13$
   $3x - 2x = 2x - 13 - 2x$ (addition property of equations)
   $x = 2x - 2x - 13$ (commutative property of addition)
   $x = -13$

2. $.5a + 36 + 4a = -9a - 12$
   $.5a + 36 + 4a - 36 = -9a - 12 - 36$ (addition property of equations)
   $.5a + 4a + 36 - 36 = -9a - 48$ (commutative property of addition)
   $4.5a = -9a - 48$
   $4.5a + 9a = -9a - 48 + 9a$ (additive property of equations)
   $13.5a = -9a + 9a - 48$ (commutative property of equations)
   $13.5a = -48$
   $a = -48/13.5$ (multiplication property of equations)

3. $5(c + 3) - 2c + 9 = 2(c - 1) + 13$
   $5c + 15 - 2c + 9 = 2c - 2 + 13$ (distributive property of multiplication over addition)
   $5c - 2c + 15 + 9 = 2c + 11$ (commutative property of equations)
   $3c + 24 = 2c + 11$
   $3c + 24 - 2c = 2c + 11 - 2c$ (addition property of equations)
   $3c - 2c + 24 = 2c - 2c + 11$ (commutative property of addition)
   $c + 24 = 11$
   $c + 24 - 24 = 11 - 24$ (additive property of equations)
   $c = -13$

Notes 8.14—Investigating Distance vs. Time Motion

MATH CONTENT

- Rate of change, distance vs. time functions, independent and dependent variables

MATERIALS

- The following set of equipment is needed for each group: a TI-82 (or TI-82 or TI-92) graphing calculator with the "Hiker" program, a Calculator-based Laboratory™ (CBL), a motion detector, a link

CONNECTIONS

- Exercises and More Problems: #54

TIMETABLE

- 45-60 minutes for activity
- 15 minutes for class discussion

ACTIVITY DISCUSSION

This activity engages the students in collecting and analyzing data that they create themselves using the equipment and their motion. The analysis of the data can help students to develop deeper a understanding of a functional relationship, and to interpret and explain what is happening at different points on the graph.

If time in class is limited, question #1 is the only one that must be done with the equipment. It will take approximately 20-30 minutes for students to do #1a-f, depending upon their familiarity with the equipment. We suggest that you demonstrate how to set up and use the equipment in front of the class before the students start working in their groups.

ACTIVITY SOLUTIONS

1. graphs will vary but some general guidelines are listed below
    a. student should walk away from the motion detector
    b. student should walk away from the motion detector at a more rapid pace than in a.
    c. student should walk toward the motion detector
    d. student should walk toward the motion detector at a slower pace than in c.
    e. student should stand still
    f. student should walk away from the motion detector rapidly, turn quickly, and walk toward the motion detector

2. a. a horizontal line; the person's distance from the motion detector is not changing
    b. the graph will be steeper if the person is running
    c. if the person is moving toward the motion detector, the slope is negative; if the person is moving away from the motion detector, the slope is positive
    d. look at the value of the y-coordinate of the initial point

3. a. the person started 2 units (e.g., feet) away from the motion detector and walk away from the motion detector at a rate of 1/2 unit per second
    b. the person started 2 units away from the motion detector, walked away from the motion detector, slowly at first and then rapidly

c. the person started 4 units away from the motion detector, walked away from the motion detector, rapidly at first and then more slowly

Chapter 9: Geometry

Chapter Overview:

Geometry is among the richest and oldest branches of mathematics. We think of geometry as the study of space experiences. This study focuses mainly on shapes as abstractions from the environment, which can be informally investigated and analyzed. In this chapter, you will explore 2-dimensional shapes (although most of the ideas are equally valid for 3-dimensional shapes as well). Particular attention is given to making conjectures and attempting to verify them—that is, to develop proofs for your conjectures.

Big Mathematical Ideas:

> problem-solving strategies, shape & space, congruence, similarity, verifying, conjecturing, generalizing, decomposing

NCTM Standards Links:

K - 4: Mathematics as problem solving; Mathematics as communication; Mathematics as reasoning; Mathematical connections; Geometry & spatial sense

5 - 8: Mathematics as problem solving; Mathematics as communication; Mathematics as reasoning; Mathematical connections; Geometry

Chapter Outline:

Notes 9.1—Communicating with Precise Language

MATH CONTENT

- mathematical language

MATERIALS

- two sets of tangrams and one set of pages 175-176 for each pair of students

CONNECTIONS

- Exercises and More Problems: #73

TIMETABLE

- 10 minutes for activity
- 5 minutes for class discussion

ACTIVITY DISCUSSION
This activity is designed to give students a chance to experience the necessity of precision in language usage. As each pair finishes, talk with them about their success/failure to duplicate the figures. Discuss problems with language with the entire class. Ask pairs to volunteer some of the problems and/or solutions they encountered during the activity.

Use the figures on the next two pages as the designs for the pairs to duplicate.

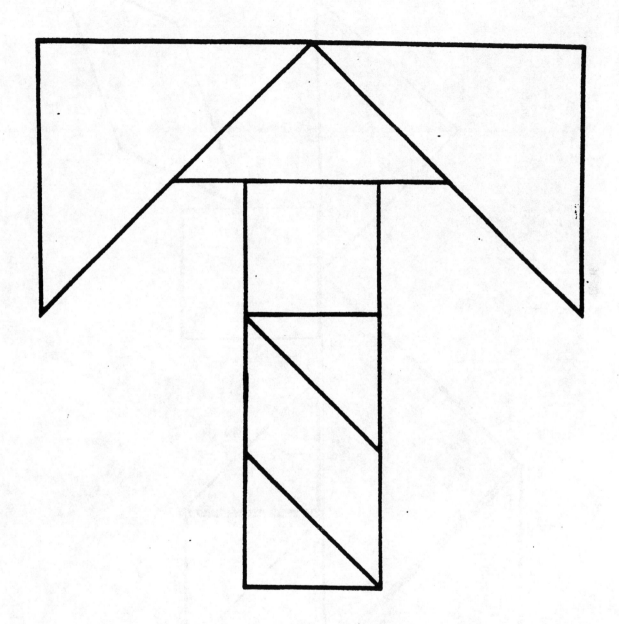

Notes 9.2—Definitions: What is Necessary and What is Sufficient?

MATH CONTENT

- mathematical language

MATERIALS

- cut out disk from page 179

CONNECTIONS

- Exercises and More Problems: #74

TIMETABLE

- 15-20 minutes for activity/class discussion

ACTIVITY DISCUSSION

Using the notes below, lead a class discussion on the definitions listed. Write the students' definitions on the board. During the discussion of what makes a good definition, look for counterexamples and/or ways to misinterpret their definitions. Writing a good definition involves both carefully considering *necessary* and *sufficient* conditions and verifying that the definition says what we think it says.

<u>Notes for Discussion of Definitions</u>
What is a good definition?

1. *Ask for the definition of a basketball (or some other common object).*

   Have the students continue to refine the definition until they are convinced that someone who has never seen a basketball before, or who has no preconceived idea about a basketball, would be able to identify one from a large group of diverse objects. The point to emphasize here is the necessity of the precision of language, and necessary and sufficient information.

2. *Ask for the definition of a circle.*

   Someone is likely to say it s the set of points equidistant from a given point (or the center). Then ask what happens when the radius is zero. You should expect them to be a little surprised about this. They may never have considered this before. Is this a point? Is it a set of infinitely many points all equidistant from a given point? As they volunteer possible solutions to this problem, discuss what conditions are necessary and sufficient to have a good definition.

   If the students do not include the word "all" in "a set of all points", draw a semicircle, or any arc of a circle, and ask them if this fits the definition. If the definition does not include the points being in the same plane, demonstrate with the cut out disk a circle in more than one plane (by bending the disk).

3. *Ask for the definition of adjacent angles.*

   Students are likely to give answers such as angles that share a common side. Draw illustrations, using the definitions they give, showing that the angles they are describing do not have to be adjacent. They important phrases for them to come up with here are angles in the same plane, share a common ray, have a common vertex, have no interior points in common.

4. *Ask for the definition of similarity.*

Students may offer loose definitions, citing same shape but different size, AA theorem, perhaps even the proportional sides definition. The problem with these definitions is that they are likely to apply only to triangles, but of course, you did not ask about similar triangles, you asked about similarity.

Draw illustrations, using the definitions they give, showing that they are not including necessary conditions. If they tell you that similar figures have the same shape but different size, draw two hexagons on the board that are definitely not similar. Explain that these are both hexagons, so they are the same shape. Are they similar? [It may be necessary to discuss the word "shape." Many times when the phrase "same shape" is used, the intent is that the objects are exactly the same. However, in geometry the phrase "same shape" refers to the same general shape (e.g., both are quadrilaterals but not necessarily of the same size or with same angle measurements). The students should recognize they are not similar, and will offer suggestions for improving the definition.

The point in doing all this is that language, especially in mathematics, is important. Definitions must be clear and unmistakable. Help students to see the importance of trying to find counterexamples and of being certain that the definition completely describes the concept to be characterized.

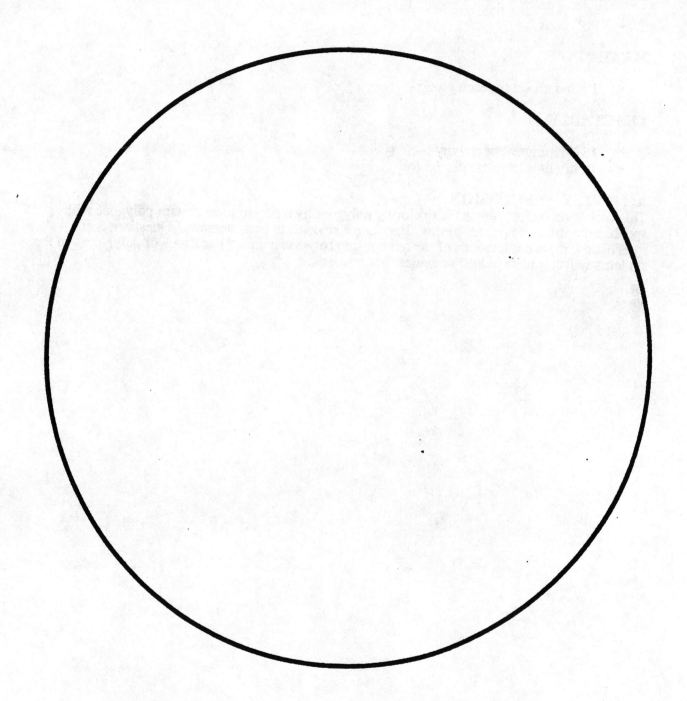

Notes 9.3—Tangram Puzzles: Exploring Geometric Shapes

MATH CONTENT

- Polygons

MATERIALS

- 1 tangram set for each group

TIMETABLE

- 15-20 minutes for activity
- 10 minutes for class discussion

ACTIVITY DISCUSSION

This activity engages students in exploring polygons by trying to form certain polygons with specific numbers of tangram pieces. Encourage students to be systematic. Questions 3 and 4 foreshadow more explorations of the relationship between perimeter and area of polygons that the students will complete in later activities.

Notes 9.4—Constructing Geometric Relationships

MATH CONTENT

- Geometric constructions

MATERIALS

- compass and straightedge for each student (students can be asked to supply these)

CONNECTIONS

- Students will need to be able to make these basic constructions for later activities.

TIMETABLE

- 15-20 minutes for activity
- 5 minutes for class discussion

ACTIVITY DISCUSSION
This activity could be done as homework. Students will need to be able to make these basic constructions for Activities 9.11, 9.12, 9.13 and some problems in Exercises and More Problems.

ACTIVITY SOLUTIONS
6.   △ BCD is an isosceles triangle

Notes 9.5—Exploring Lines and Angles

MATH CONTENT

- Angles, parallel lines

MATERIALS

- paper triangles of various sizes and types (one for each student or pair)

TIMETABLE

- 20 minutes for activity
- 5-10 minutes for class discussion

ACTIVITY DISCUSSION

Make sure students know how to do the activity; you may want to demonstrate how to place the triangle and trace. Discuss how the kind of triangle used is immaterial—the results are the same. Have students explain how they can prove from their work that the sum of the measures of the angles of a triangle equals 180°.

ACTIVITY SOLUTIONS

1. parallel, congruent
2. parallel, congruent
3. the sum of the interior angles of a triangle is 180°
4. answers will vary
5. they are congruent
6. they are supplementary
7. they are always true; students' explanations will vary
8. <3 and <7, <4 and <8, <2 and <6
9. <4 and <5
10. <1 and <8
11. the corresponding angles are congruent, the alternate interior angles are congruent
12. they are always true; students' explanations will vary

Notes 9.6—Defining Angles and Lines

MATH CONTENT

- Various types of angles, points, parallel lines, perpendicular lines, plane, precision of language

TIMETABLE

- 10 minutes for activity
- 10 minutes for class discussion

ACTIVITY DISCUSSION

Divide the 12 concepts to be defined into more or less equal groups so that you can assign one group of concepts to two groups of students. (For example if you have 8 groups of students, have 4 concept groups of 3 concepts each—two groups discuss #1, 5 & 9; two groups discuss #2, 6 & 10; two groups discuss #3, 7 & 11; two groups discuss #4, 8, 12.)

After the groups have worked on their concepts, call on them to give their definitions. This will be a good time to review the ideas from Activity 9.2, especially the use of counterexamples. Encourage students to question inadequate definitions and give counterexamples.

ACTIVITY SOLUTIONS

The definitions below assume that one has already defined an angle (an angle is formed when two rays in a plane are joined at a common endpoint).

1. an angle that measures exactly 90°
2. an angle with measure x, such that $0 < x < 90°$
3. an angle with measure x, such that $90 < x < 180°$
4. angles that share a common vertex and ray, and have no common interior points
5. a pair of angles whose angle sum is 90°
6. a pair of angles whose angle sum is 180°
7. a pair of angles formed by two intersecting lines who share only a vertex
8. a pair of angles formed by two intersecting lines who share a vertex and ray
9. points that lie on the same line
10. points that lie in the same plane
11. coplanar lines that do not intersect
12. lines that intersect to form right angles

Notes 9.7—Exploring Polygons

MATH CONTENT

- Polygons, triangles, quadrilaterals, regular polygon, convex polygon, concave polygon

TIMETABLE

- 10 minutes for activity
- 10 minutes for class discussion

ACTIVITY DISCUSSION

This activity engages students in defining polygons and in exploring some specific polygons—regular, concave, convex.

ACTIVITY SOLUTIONS

1. a. a polygon is a closed plane figure composed entirely of line segments
    b. answers will vary; some are: pentagons, hexagons, heptagons, octagons, nonagons, decagons
    c. square
    d. i. answers will vary   ii. triangle

Notes 9.8—Exploring Quadrilaterals

MATH CONTENT

- Quadrilaterals, properties of quadrilaterals

CONNECTIONS

- This activity leads into Activity 9.9 and should be completed before it.

TIMETABLE

- 10 minutes for activity
- 5 minutes for class discussion

ACTIVITY DISCUSSION

This activity engages students in identifying some properties of specific quadrilaterals and could be done as homework before doing Activity 9.9 in class.

ACTIVITY SOLUTIONS

1. all but 7, 9, and 10 (i.e., 1, 2, 3, 4, 5, 6, 8, 11, 12)
2. 2, 3, 4, 5, 6, 11, 12
3. 1, 3, 4, 6, 12
4. 2, 3, 5, 6, 7, 10
5. a. 2, 3, 4, 5, 6, 11, 12
   b. 3, 6
   c. all
   d. using the definition that a trapezoid is a quadrilateral with at least one pair of parallel sides:
      1, 2, 3, 4, 5, 6, 8, 11, 12
   e. 3, 4, 6, 12
   f. 2, 3, 5, 6, 7, 10
   g. 2, 3, 5, 6
   h. 1, 2, 3, 4, 5, 6, 11, 12
6. a. some
   b. some
   c. all
   d. all
   e. some

Notes 9.9—Properties of Quadrilaterals

MATH CONTENT

- Quadrilaterals, properties of quadrilaterals

CONNECTIONS

- Exercises and More Problems: #63-65

TIMETABLE

- 20-30 minutes for activity
- 10 minutes for class discussion

ACTIVITY DISCUSSION

This is an important activity that will help students understand the relationships among special types of quadrilaterals. You may want to have students use tools like *Geometer's Sketchpad*™, geoboards, compasses and straightedges, etc. in exploring what properties certain quadrilaterals possess.

ACTIVITY SOLUTIONS

1. see next page
2.

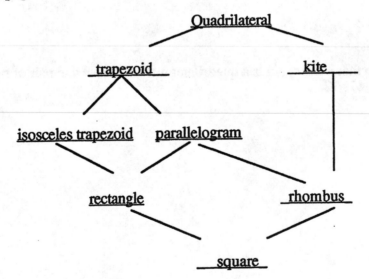

3. as you move down the tree diagram, the quadrilaterals possess more side properties
4. as you move down the tree diagram, the quadrilaterals possess more diagonal properties
5. answers will vary

PROPERTIES	QUADRILATERALS						
	Parallelogram	Rectangle	Rhombus	Square	Trapezoid	Isosc. Trap.	Kite
Side Properties							
4 sides	X	X	X	X	X	X	X
At least 1 pair of parallel sides	X	X	X	X	X	X	X
2 pairs of parallel sides	X	X	X	X			
All sides congruent			X	X			
At least one pair of opposite sides congruent	X	X	X	X		X	
Opposite sides congruent	X	X	X	X			
2 pairs of congruent adjacent sides			X	X			X
Angle Properties							
Interior angle sum = 360°	X	X	X	X	X	X	X
All angles are right angles		X		X			
Opposite angles are congruent	X	X	X	X			
Adjacent angles are supplementary	X	X	X	X			
Diagonal Properties							
Diagonals bisect each other	X	X	X	X			
Diagonals are congruent		X		X			X
Diagonals are perpendicular			X	X			X
Diagonals bisect vertex angles			X	X			X
1 diagonal forms 2 congruent triangles	X	X	X	X		X	X
Diagonals form 4 congruent triangles				X			
Symmetric Properties							
Number of lines of symmetry	0	2	2	4	0	1	1
Rotational Symmetry	180°	180°	180°	90°, 180° 270°	none	none	none

Notes 9.10—Defining Triangles

MATH CONTENT

- Triangles, special types of triangles

CONNECTIONS

- Exercises and More Problems: #77

TIMETABLE

- 10 minutes for activity
- 5 minutes for class discussion

ACTIVITY DISCUSSION

Divide the 8 terms among the groups so that two groups will be defining the same set of terms. (For example, with 8 groups, have 4 sets of 2 terms each.) This should be a quick activity as a result. Make sure they share their definitions. Encourage students to challenge incorrect definitions and provide counterexamples.

ACTIVITY SOLUTIONS

1. a triangle with one right angle
2. a triangle with all acute angles
3. a triangle with one obtuse angle
4. a triangle with no congruent sides
5. a triangle with at least two congruent sides
6. a triangle with three congruent sides
7. a segment drawn from one vertex to the midpoint of the opposite side
8. a segment drawn from one vertex perpendicular to the opposite side

Notes 9.11—Exploring Side Lengths in Triangles

MATH CONTENT

- Triangles, relationship among the lengths of the sides (Triangle Inequality)

MATERIALS

- Students will need compasses, straightedges, blank paper and protractors.

CONNECTIONS

- Exercises and More Problems: #66-68

TIMETABLE

- 10 minutes for activity
- 10 minutes for class discussion

ACTIVITY DISCUSSION

This activity gives the students some experience with the Triangle Inequality. As the students are constructing the triangles, ask them to discuss why these constructions are valid (e.g., how do they know they are really constructing a congruent angle). It will not take them long to find that some of the triangles cannot be formed. Encourage them to write the results anyway. Ask students to write their observation in the form of a theorem.

Watch for correct mathematical vocabulary and for correct formulation of the conjecture and theorem. Give them ample opportunity to correct their own mistakes. Discuss the structure of theorems (hypothesis-conclusion form). Many students think that only statements written in if-then form are theorems. Emphasize that all theorems can be written in this form but do not have to be written in if-then form.

ACTIVITY SOLUTIONS

1. not possible
2. not possible
3. not possible
4. possible
5.

Side lengths a, b, c	a + b	b + c	c + a	What happened?
2, 3, 5	5	8	7	not possible
2, 3, 6	5	9	8	not possible
3, 4, 10	7	14	13	not possible
4, 6, 7	10	13	11	possible

6. If $a + b > c$, then a triangle can be constructed.

Notes 9.12—Exploring Triangle Congruence

MATH CONTENT

- Triangle congruence

MATERIALS

- Students will need compasses, straightedges, blank paper and protractors.

TIMETABLE

- 20 minutes for activity
- 10 minutes for class discussion

ACTIVITY DISCUSSION

This activity gives the students some experience with several triangle congruence relationships—the SSS Theorem and the SAS Theorem. As the students are constructing the triangles, ask them to discuss why these constructions are valid (e.g., how do they know they are really constructing a congruent angle). Ask students to write a conjecture/generalization that they can verify as they proceed through the activity.

Watch for correct mathematical vocabulary and for correct formulation of the conjecture and theorem. Give them ample opportunity to correct their own mistakes. Discuss the structure of theorems (hypothesis-conclusion form). Many students think that only statements written in if-then form are theorems. Emphasize that all theorems can be written in this form but do not have to be written in if-then form.

ACTIVITY SOLUTIONS

1. congruent triangles are triangles that have all corresponding angles and sides congruent
2. they are congruent
3. $1 \text{ in} < x < 5 \text{ in}$
4. If three sides of one triangle are congruent to three sides of another triangle
5. Then the two triangles are congruent.
6. If three sides of one triangle are congruent to three sides of another triangle, then the two triangles are congruent.
   Side-Side-Side Theorem (SSS)
7. they are congruent
8. they are congruent
9. they are not congruent
10. If two sides and the included angle of one triangle are congruent to two sides and the included angle of another triangle, then the two triangles are congruent.
    Side-Angle-Side Theorem (SAS)

Notes 9.13—Exploring Triangle Similarity

MATH CONTENT

- Triangle similarity

MATERIALS

- Students will need compasses, straightedges, blank paper and protractors.

CONNECTIONS

- Exercises and More Problems: #69

TIMETABLE

- 25 minutes for activity
- 15 minutes for class discussion

ACTIVITY DISCUSSION

This activity gives the students some experience with similarity ideas—specifically triangle similarity. As the students are constructing the triangles, ask them to discuss why these constructions are valid (e.g., how do they know they are really constructing a congruent angle). Ask students to write a conjecture/generalization that they can verify as they proceed through the activity.

Watch for correct mathematical vocabulary and for correct formulation of the conjecture and theorem. Give them ample opportunity to correct their own mistakes. During the discussion, have students articulate what it means for two triangles to be similar, and for two polygons to be similar.

ACTIVITY SOLUTIONS

2. there are these relationships: sides are proportional, angles are congruent (triangles are similar); note the importance of corresponding sides
3. answers will vary
4. sides are proportional, angles are congruent (triangles are similar)

Notes 9.14—More On Similarity

MATH CONTENT

- Similarity, dilation

MATERIALS

- Overhead projector, polygons on overhead transparencies

CONNECTIONS

- Exercises and More Problems: #70, 75

TIMETABLE

- 30 minutes for activity/class discussion

ACTIVITY DISCUSSION

This activity has students explore similarity and dilation through an interactive class discussion. In discussing #1, encourage students to articulate what it means to be similar. Ask questions such as, are all quadrilaterals similar? are all parallelograms similar? are all rectangles similar? are all squares similar?

Students should be able to identify the overhead projector as the machine that dilates figures and that the dilation is an enlargement. Turn on the projector and display various shapes on overhead transparencies, geometric or otherwise. Have students discover how angles and equality and inequality (greater or less) of sides are preserved. For a simple shape such as a square, have them estimate how much larger a side is and the area is to those of the original and note these estimates down. Ask how the shape could be enlarged further or the present enlargement reduced. Move the projector as needed. Again get estimates based on the square figure.

Have students realize that the <u>scale of dilation</u> is changed by the distance from the projector to the dilated image (on screen). Say that the position of the projector corresponds to what is called the <u>center of dilation</u> in some methods for constructing similar figures.

Go back to their estimates (at least 3 sets) and say that a length which was n times the original indicates a scale factor of n/1. (If possible, get them to see the area ratio is approximately $n^2/1$.)

Notes 9.15—Constructing Proofs

MATH CONTENT

- Proof, relationships in triangles and quadrilateral

MATERIALS

- Students will need compasses, straightedges and blank paper

CONNECTIONS

- Exercises and More Problems: #71-72, 76

TIMETABLE

- 45 minutes for activity
- 20 minutes for class discussion

ACTIVITY DISCUSSION

This activity involves students in proving some relationships and is a good activity for students to complete before later activities involving proofs. It is very important to have a class discussion on "What is proof?" before beginning the activity. Questions you can pose include: Is measuring sufficient? Is measuring only concerned with specific cases or can it be used to prove something in general? What is necessary to prove something? What is sufficient? [use an example here] What does it mean to say we have the necessary and sufficient information to prove something? The important thing to stress during this activity is the process of verification.

The activity starts with some straightforward proofs and culminates in #4, which uses the theorem proved in #3. Have the students refer to the theorems in the Explanations Concerning Geometry in Chapter 9 of the *Resource Manual* for ones that can be used in proofs. Note that #1-3 are listed in the Explanations but are being proved in this activity. It may be necessary to do the first proof together as a class. Emphasize the ideas of generalizing and verifying and how they are used in this activity.

ACTIVITY SOLUTIONS

1. Draw △ ABC with sides AB and BC congruent. Draw ray BD which bisects <B and intersects side AC. Then △ ABD is congruent to △ CBD by the SAS theorem. Thus, <A is congruent to <C since corresponding parts of congruent triangles are congruent (CPCTC).

2. Draw quadrilateral ABCD with sides AB and DC congruent, and AD and BC congruent. Draw diagonal BD. Then △ ABD is congruent to △ CDB by the SSS theorem. By CPCTC, <ABD is congruent to <CDB and <ADB is congruent to <CBD. Then side AB is parallel to side DC and side AD is parallel to side BC because if two lines are cut by a transversal and the alternate interior angles are congruent, the lines are parallel. Thus, quadrilateral ABCD is a parallelogram by definition of a parallelogram (two pairs of opposite sides parallel).

3. Draw △ ABC and draw segment DE, where D is the midpoint of side AC and E is the midpoint of side AB. Then sides AD and AE are 1/2 of sides AC and AB, respectively (definition of midpoint). △ AED and △ ABC are similar by the SAS similarity theorem. This gives us <ADE and <ACB congruent (similar triangles have all angles congruent). Thus, side DE is parallel to side CB because if two lines are cut by a transversal and the corresponding angles are congruent, the lines are parallel.

4. Each side of quadrilateral EFGH is the hypotenuse of a 45°-45°-90° triangle and the legs of these triangles are all 1/2 the length of a side of ABCD. Thus, all the sides of EFGH are congruent. At each vertex of EFGH there are two 45° angles plus the vertex angle. Since the three angles together are 180°, the vertex angles must be 90°. Thus, EFGH is a square.

Notes 9.16—Sums of Measures of Angles of Polygons

MATH CONTENT

- Relationship among the number of sides and the sum of the measures of the angles in a polygon

MATERIALS

- Students will need compasses, straightedges, protractors and blank paper

CONNECTIONS

- Exercises and More Problems: #78

TIMETABLE

- 25 minutes for activity
- 15 minutes for class discussion

ACTIVITY DISCUSSION

This activity involves students in investigating the sum of the measures of the angles of any polygon. It may be helpful to review what results they may need to use: Euclidean Parallel Postulate, SAS theorem, SSS theorem, ASA theorem, CPCTC, parallel lines cut by transversal have alternate interior angles congruent, etc. They should be arriving at a generalization and the verification of this generalization. Look for two or more different student explanations/proofs. in this activity, one of the goals is to establish what proof means to different people.

It is important to stop after both #1 and #2 and discuss the groups' plans and proofs. The following is a sample dialogue between a group of students and a teacher.

T: The only way you can prove anything is by using results that you already know. You need to think if what you're trying to prove relates in any way to something you know.

S: What about the fact that linear angles on a line add up to 180°? A line has 180° and a Δ in a bent line. Is that a proof?

T: You can take a line and bend it into anything—into a circle, and that's 360°. Or into a square, and that's 360°.

Some methods of proof that might be used include the paper-tearing approach and the parallel lines approach discussed below.

Paper-tearing Approach

The sum of the measures of the angles in a triangle can intuitively be shown to be 180° by tearing the three angles off a triangle, and placing them along a line with the vertices together. Because the sum of the measures of the angles equals the measure of a straight angle, then the sum of the measures of the angles of a triangle is 180°.

Parallel Lines Approach

To prove that the sum of the measures of the angles of a triangle is 180°, consider triangle XYZ below. To prove that m<1 + m<2 + m<3 = 180°, we will show that the sum of the measures of the three angles is the same as the measure of a straight angle. Draw line k parallel to side XZ. Since k and side XZ are parallel with transversals XY and ZY, the alternate interior angles are congruent. Thus, m<4 = m<3 and m<5 = m<1. Then m<1 + m<2 + m<3 = m<5 + m<2 + m<4, but since this last sum is of linear angles, the sum is 180°. Thus, m<1 + m<2 + m<3 = 180°.

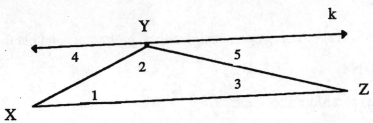

Discuss the merits of each process. Which "proof" would a third-grader accept? Which proof would a mathematician accept? (It is important to note that mathematicians do not accept hand waving as easily as many prospective elementary teachers.) Which one do your students accept? Is the paper-tearing approach generalizable or is it specific to triangle examples?

Ask for demonstrations of the process students used to find the sum of the measures of the angles of a polygon. Have them give a verbal expression of the generalization as well as the formula in mathematical symbols. Some methods of proof that might be used include drawing all diagonals from a given vertex or drawing segments to each vertex from an interior point.

Some students may already know the generalized formula [(n - 2) • 180], but have them verify why this formula works. Why 180? Where does the n - 2 come from? How do you know that a polygon with 1000 sides will be divided into 998 triangles (if the diagonals are drawn from one vertex)? Bring out the idea of decomposition in breaking the polygon into triangles to find the sum of the measures.

Question 3 is an important question to discuss. The students may first need to discuss the difference between regular and non-regular polygons. A good question to pose is "Can the last column of the chart on page 299 be found for non-regular polygons?"

ACTIVITY SOLUTIONS

1. see above discussion
2. see above discussion and table on next page
3. the sum of the angle measurements is the same because the triangles can be formed regardless
4. the relationship does not hold for concave polygons because sometimes distinct diagonals cannot be drawn

Polygon	# of Sides	Sum of Angle Measurements	Measurement of Each Angle if Polygon is Regular
Triangle	3	180°	60°
Square	4	360°	90°
Pentagon	5	540°	108°
Hexagon	6	720°	120°
Heptagon	7	900°	(900/7)° ≈ 128.6°
Octagon	8	1080°	135°
Nonagon	9	1260°	140°
Decagon	10	1440°	144°
11-gon	11	1620°	(1620/11)° ≈ 147.3°
Dodecagon	12	1800°	150°
13-gon	13	1980°	(1980/13)° ≈ 152.3°
57-gon	57	9900°	(9900/57)° ≈ 173.7°
89-gon	89	15660	(15660/89)° ≈ 175.9°
n-gon	n	(n - 2)180	(n - 2)180/n

Notes 9.17—Spherical Geometry

MATH CONTENT

- Spherical geometry, great circle, angle measure on a sphere

CONNECTIONS

- Exercises and More Problems: #79, 80

TIMETABLE

- 15 minutes for activity
- 10 minutes for class discussion

ACTIVITY DISCUSSION

This activity engages students in exploring a non-Euclidean geometry and challenges their conception that the sum of the angle measures in a triangle is always 180°. You may want to have students read the Historical/Social/Cultural Notes about Geometry before completing this activity.

ACTIVITY SOLUTIONS

1. true in Euclidean geometry
2. true in Euclidean geometry
3. true in Euclidean geometry
4. a circle that is formed by a plane through the center of the sphere intersecting the sphere (e.g., the equator)
5. yes, the circumference of the sphere
6. two, because they will cross on opposite sides of the sphere
7. yes
8. cannot be determined
9. yes, infinitely many
10. yes, the lines like the latitude lines
11. no
12. greater than 180°
13. one right angle in Euclidean geometry
14. a triangle can have two right angles in spherical geometry because the great circles that contain two of the sides can both be perpendicular to the third side
15. one
16. 360°

Chapter 10: Measurement

Chapter Overview:

Perhaps no part of mathematics is more clearly applicable to everyday life than measurement, the focus of the activities in this chapter. As a consequence of the practicality of measurement in the real world, it is a very important strand in the elementary school mathematics curriculum. In particular, students learn extremely useful measurement skills (e.g., how to use a ruler), concepts (e.g., the concepts of area and perimeter), and key formulas (e.g., $A = 1 \cdot w$). Just as important is the fact that making measurements can be a source of many, very interesting problems. For example, did you know that two shapes can have the same perimeter, but different areas? One natural question that follows from this is can two shapes have the same area, but different perimeters? In this chapter you will investigate these and many other challenging problems.

Big Mathematical Ideas:

> problem-solving strategies, conjecturing; verifying; generalizing

NCTM Standards Links:

> **K - 4:** Mathematics as problem solving; Mathematics as communication; Mathematics as reasoning; Mathematical connections; Measurement

> **5 - 8:** Mathematics as problem solving; Mathematics as communication; Mathematics as reasoning; Mathematical connections; Measurement

Chapter Outline:

Notes 10.1:	Exploring Area and Perimeter
Notes 10.2:	Perimeter and Area: Is There a Relationship?
Notes 10.3:	Pick's Formula
Notes 10.4:	Investigating Length
Notes 10.5:	Pythagoras and Proof
Notes 10.6:	Investigating Circles
Notes 10.7:	Investigating the Circumference to Diameter Ratio
Notes 10.8:	Investigating the Area of a Circle
Notes 10.9:	Surface Area and Volume of Rectangular Prisms
Notes 10.10:	Drawing Rectangular Prisms
Notes 10.11:	Exploring the Surface Area of Cones
Notes 10.12:	Investigating the Volumes of Cylinders and Cones
Notes 10.13:	Geoboard Battleship: Exploring Coordinate Geometry
Notes 10.14:	Investigating Translations using *Sketchpad*™
Notes 10.15:	Investigating Rotations using *Sketchpad*™
Notes 10.16:	Investigating Reflections using *Sketchpad*™
Notes 10.17:	Tessellations: One Definition
Notes 10.18:	Tessellations: Another Definition

Notes 10.1—Exploring Area and Perimeter

MATH CONTENT

- Area, perimeter

CONNECTIONS

- Exercises and More Problems: #54-55

TIMETABLE

- 15 minutes for activity
- 5 minutes for class discussion

ACTIVITY DISCUSSION

Have students share their demonstration of the proof that $A = xy$ and draw a picture to go with their description of the proof. Discuss the idea of *deduction* and have a student deduce that $A = s^2$ from $A = xy$ and $P = 4s$ from $P = 2(x + y)$ taking $x = s$ and $y = s$ when the rectangle is a square.

Different strategies for finding the area of the polygon could be discussed from the students' work. If they use the area formula for a right triangle, ask how it can be deduced from that for rectangles.

ACTIVITY SOLUTIONS

1. 1 square inch; 1 square mile
2. there are x squares in one row and there are y rows; so there are $A = x + x + \ldots + x$, where x is written y times; so $A = xy$ (viewing multiplication as repeated addition)

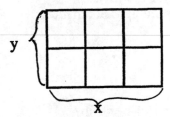

3. if $x = s$ and $y = s$, then $A = s^2$
4. a. $P = 2(x + y)$; $P = x + y + x + y = x + x + y + y = 2x + 2y = 2(x + y)$
   b. if $x = s$ and $y = s$, then $P = 2(s + s) = 2 (2s) = 4s$
5. 51 cm^2

Notes 10.2—Area and Perimeter: Is There a Relationship?

MATH CONTENT

- Area, perimeter

MATERIALS

- 30 color tiles per group, one geoboard with rubber bands per group

CONNECTIONS

- Exercises and More Problems: #68

TIMETABLE

- 15 minutes for activity/class discussion for building rectangles
- 15 minutes for geoboard activity
- 10 minutes for class discussion

ACTIVITY DISCUSSION

The question motivating this activity is, "Is there a relationship between area and perimeter of polygons?" During the rectangle building activity, ask groups to build the different rectangles. You may want to pick and choose ones to assign. For each set of conditions, have the students find as many rectangles as possible that meet the conditions. Some particularly interesting discussion can be generated by #9, 10, 14, 15, 18, 19 and 20.

As the students work with the geoboards, pay attention to what they call 1 unit. It is common for them to believe that the distance between any two pegs is 1 unit (even when it is on the diagonal). In order to have them measure a diagonal's length, ask them to use their compasses to compare the length of 1 unit and the length of a diagonal. If students what to know the length of the diagonal, remind them of the Pythagorean theorem, which they should know from middle school and high school.

Encourage students to be systematic in investigating the relationship between area and perimeter on the geoboard. By making an organized list (i.e., looking at polygons with the same areas and different perimeters, then same perimeter and different areas) and looking for a pattern, students will come to the conclusion that no generalization exists relating perimeter and area. However, in Activity 10.3 (Pick's formula), students will find that there is a relationship between area and perimeter if the boundary and interior points of the polygon on a geoboard are considered.

ACTIVITY SOLUTIONS
Rectangle Building
1. 1 x 11, 1 x 12, 2 x 6, 3 x 4, 1 x 13, 1 x 14, 2 x 7, 1 x 15, 3 x 5
2. 2 x 3, 1 x 4, 2 x 4, 3 x 4, 1 x 5, 1 x 6, 2 x 5, 3 x 4
3. 1 x 1, 1 x 2, 1 x 3, etc.
4. 3 x 6, 4 x 4
5. 7 x 3, 8 x 3, 9 x 3, 5 x 4, etc.
6. odd # x even #, even # x even #
7. all rectangles
8. odd # x odd #
9. not possible
10. 1 x 4, 1 x 9, 1 x 16, 2 x 8, 1 x 25

11. 1 x 1, 1 x 3, 2 x 2, 1 x 5, 3 x 3, 1 x 7, 2 x 6, 3 x 5, 1 x 9, 2 x 8, 3 x 7, 5 x 5, 1 x 11,
     2 x 10, 3 x 9, 5 x 7, 6 x 6, 1 x 13, 2 x 12, 3 x 11, 5 x 9, 6 x 8, 7 x 7
12. 1 x 30
13. 1 x 19
14. 4 x 4
15. 1 x 16
16. 2 x 6
17. 1 x 3, 1 x 5, 1 x 7, 1 x 11, 1 x 13, 1 x 17, 1 x 19, 1 x 23, 1 x 29
18. not possible
19. 7 x 3
20. 4 x 8, 5 x 5, 6 x 4, 9 x 3

Geoboard Activity

The following table may be helpful in generating questions for the class discussion.

Perimeter (units)	\multicolumn{12}{c}{Number of polygons with given perimeter and area — Area (square units)}

Perimeter (units)	1	2	3	4	5	6	7	8	9	10	11	12
4	1											
6		1										
8			2	1								
10				4	1	1						
12			3	4	12	8	4	2	1			
14				4	12	38	32	30	12	7	1	1

The following reference gives geoboard diagrams of polygons with the perimeters and areas in the table.

Reference

Smith, L. R. (1990). Areas and perimeters of geoboard polygons. *Mathematics Teacher, 83* (5), 392-399.

Notes 10.3—Pick's Formula

MATH CONTENT

- Area, perimeter

MATERIALS

- One geoboard with rubber bands per group

CONNECTIONS

- Exercises and More Problems: #56-58, 67

TIMETABLE

- 30 minutes for activity
- 10 minutes for class discussion

ACTIVITY DISCUSSION

The question motivating this activity is again, "Is there a relationship between area and perimeter of polygons?" We found in Activity 10.2 that there is no direct relationship between area and perimeter of polygons in general. However, there is a relationship if we consider the polygons on a lattice and make use of interior and boundary points.

Be sure to point out, after the students have found Pick's formula, that they have not verified the formula, only generated it. Discuss how the ideas of decomposition and multiple representations are present in the activities in 10.2 and 10.3 [break down polygons into parts to find area; polygons of same perimeter or area can be represented differently].

ACTIVITY SOLUTIONS

Pick's formula is $A = I + B/2 - 1$

Notes 10.4—Investigating Length

MATH CONTENT

- Area, length

CONNECTIONS

- This activity sets up Activity 10.5 which proves the Pythagorean theorem.
- Exercises and More Problems: #66

TIMETABLE

- 30 minutes for activity
- 10 minutes for class discussion

ACTIVITY DISCUSSION

This activity involves students in finding the areas of squares for which they do not know the side lengths. Encourage students to use the lattice to find the area and then find the length of the side length. Some students will already know the Pythagorean relationship and will use this to find the side length and then the area. Ask them to find the area and side length in a different way.

ACTIVITY SOLUTIONS

1. Area = 18 square units
   side length = $3\sqrt{2}$ units
2. Area = 17 square units
   side length = $\sqrt{17}$ units
3. Area = 5 square units
   side length = $\sqrt{5}$ units
4. decompose the square into triangles and/or squares that you can find the area of, then sum up these areas to find the area of the square; once you have the area of the square, take the square root to find the length of its side
5. yes, but it helps to draw the lattice points in
   Area = 7 square units
   side length = $\sqrt{7}$ units
6. hypotenuse = $\sqrt{5}$ units

Notes 10.5—Pythagoras and Proof

MATH CONTENT

- Pythagorean relationship

CONNECTIONS

- Exercises and More Problems: #59-62, 65, 69-70

TIMETABLE

- 30 minutes for activity
- 20 minutes for group presentations
- 20 minutes for Pythagorean Extensions

ACTIVITY DISCUSSION

Introduce the activity by showing the meaning of the Pythagorean theorem—the sum of the square on the hypotenuse is equal to the sum of the squares on the other two sides. An illustration of a right triangle with squares on the sides is included here so that an overhead transparency can be made. Next, prove (with class participation) a common proof of the Pythagorean theorem. The proof statement and figure are provided in the teacher notes so that an overhead transparency can be made to be used during the proof.

<u>Proof for class discussion</u>

Let A_1 be the square composed of the two squares with sides of lengths a and b, respectively, and the four triangles that have sides of lengths a and b. Let A_2 be the square composed of the square with sides of length c, and the four triangles that have sides of lengths a and b. Then the area of A_1 = $a^2 + b^2 + 2ab$ and the area of $A_2 = c^2 + 2ab$. Now, $A_1 = A_2$ because they are both equal to $(a + b)^2$. Thus, $a^2 + b^2 + 2ab = c^2 + 2ab$, and so $a^2 + b^2 = c^2$.

Discuss why it is necessary to verify this theorem [this theorem has become so commonplace that many students accept it as a given rather than something that can be proven].

After this introduction, assign each group one of the proofs #2-7. Be prepared to help each group start their proofs. Make sure that students give reasons for the various steps of their proof and determine that triangles are congruent and that figures that look like squares are squares. The point here is to bring out the big mathematical idea of proof. Many students believe there is exactly one way to prove a theorem. (In fact, many of them believe that in mathematics there is exactly one way to do everything.) Doing different versions of a proof of the same theorem may help to dispel that notion. You can choose not to do all of the proofs, depending upon your students. In this case, different groups can do the same proof.

After working on the proofs, have students demonstrate their proofs on the board. Point out similarities and differences in the first few proofs, guiding students so that they will be able to do the same for the last few proofs. Point out that there is more than one way to prove almost everything in mathematics. The idea of multiple representations is present here in a different form than in other activities.

Eventually, lead students into a discussion about what constitutes proof. If very few people agree that someone has proven something (much like DeBrange and the Bieberbach conjecture), has it been proven? Is a proof only a proof when we all agree that it is? Or does proof exist independent of the practitioners in a field? Are verification and proof the same thing?

For the extensions of the Pythagorean theorem, you can assign this as homework, have everyone work on all of the extensions, or assign several groups to each of the three figures. Have them explore whether the figures are additive (i.e., I + II = III). Although the calculations are straightforward, the Pythagorean theorem needs to be used to demonstrate additivity. It may come as quite a surprise to students that areas are additive for sets of figures other than squares. See if students can notice something more general than squareness that accounts for additivity [the shapes are similar]. Have the class consider rephrasing the Pythagorean theorem in a more general form. A possible conjecture is as follows: If three similar figures are constructed on three sides of a right triangle, then the areas are additive; that is, the sum of the areas on the legs equals the area on the hypotenuse.

ACTIVITY SOLUTIONS
Extensions of Pythagorean Theorem
In each case, I + II = III

1. $a(a/2) + b(b/2) = c(c/2)$ since $a^2 + b^2 = c^2$
2. $(1/2)a \times a + (1/2)b \times b = (1/2)c \times c$ since $a^2 + b^2 = c^2$
3. $(1/2)\pi(a/2)^2 + (1/2)\pi(b/2)^2 = (1/2)\pi(c/2)^2$ since $a^2 + b^2 = c^2$

Proof #2   The areas A_1 and A_2 of the two squares are equal.
$A_1 = b^2 + a^2 + 4(1/2)ab$ and $A_2 = c^2 + 4(1/2)ab$
Result follows. The fact that the figure with sides of length c is a square has to be verified.

Proof #3   Let A_1 be the area of the figure as shown. Let A_2 be the sum of the areas of the two squares with sides of length a and b respectively. Let A_3 be the area of the square of side length c. The fact that this figure is a square has to be verified.

$A_1 - A_2 = 2(1/2)ab = ab$ and $A_1 - A_3 = 2(1/2)ab = ab$

Thus $A_1 - A_2 = A_1 - A_3$ so $A_2 = A_3$

thus $a^2 + b^2 = c^2$

Proof #4   Let A_1 be the sum of the areas of the three triangles. Let A_2 be the area of the trapezoid. The fact that the triangle with sides of length c is a right triangle needs to be verified.

$A_1 = (1/2)ab + (1/2)c^2 + (1/2)ab = (1/2)(c^2 + 2ab)$
$A_2 = (a + b)(b + a)/2 = [(a + b)^2]/2 = (a^2 + 2ab + b^2)/2$

Since $A_1 = A_2$, $(c^2 + 2ab)/2 = (a^2 + 2ab + b^2)/2$
Thus $c^2 = a^2 + b^2$

Proof #5   The inside figure of side length a-b is a square since all sides are congruent, and at each vertex the exterior angle is 90° which makes the interior angle 90°.

$$c^2 = 4(1/2)ab + (a - b)^2$$
$$= 2ab + a^2 - 2ab + b^2$$
$$= a^2 + b^2$$

Proof #6   The fact that the figure with sides of length c is a square needs to be verified.

$$c^2 = 4(1/2)ab + [(a + b) - 2a]^2$$
$$= 2ab + (a + b)^2 - 4a(a + b) + 4a^2$$
$$= 2ab + a^2 + 2ab + b^2 - 4a^2 - 4ab + 4a^2$$
$$= a^2 + b^2$$

Proof #7   Show that $\triangle ABC \sim \triangle ACD \sim \triangle CBD$ (AA theorem)

Since $\triangle ABC \sim \triangle ACD$, $\dfrac{AB}{AC} = \dfrac{AC}{AD}$, so $\dfrac{c}{b} = \dfrac{b}{c - x}$ or $c^2 - cx = b^2$

Since $\triangle ABC \sim \triangle CBD$, $\dfrac{AB}{BC} = \dfrac{CB}{BD}$, so $\dfrac{c}{a} = \dfrac{a}{x}$ or $cx = a^2$

Therefore $c^2 - a^2 = b^2$

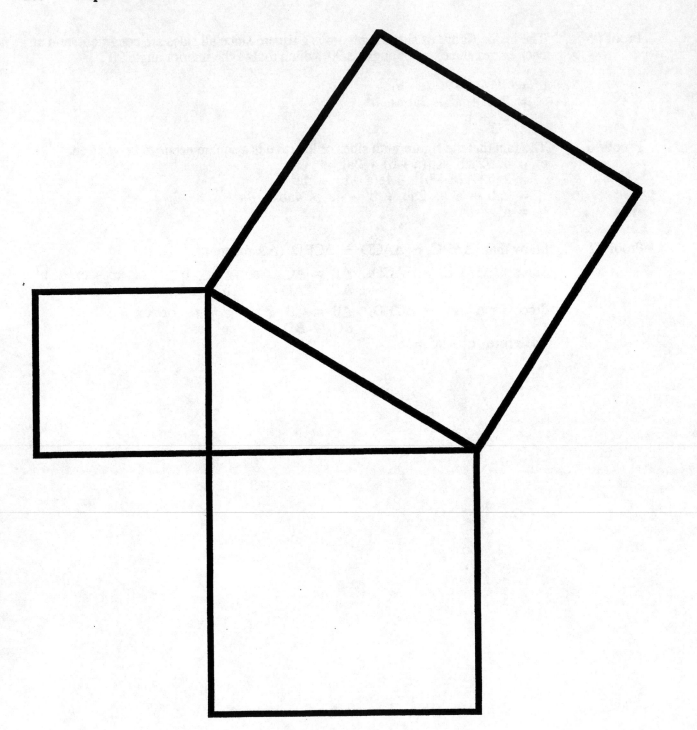

Notes 10.6—Investigating Circles

MATH CONTENT

- Circles, parts of circles

CONNECTIONS

- Exercises and More Problems: #66

TIMETABLE

- 15 minutes for activity
- 5-10 minutes for class discussion

ACTIVITY DISCUSSION

As with other activities that have involved defining terms, you can assign several terms to each group, or you can have each group define all six. During the discussion, have different groups share their definitions and encourage other students to critique them for necessary and sufficient information.

ACTIVITY SOLUTIONS

1. a segment with endpoints on a circle that contains points in the interior of the circle
2. a chord that contains the center of a circle
3. a segment or line that intersects a circle in exactly two points and contains points in the exterior of the circle
4. a segment or line that intersects a circle in exactly one point and contains no points in the interior of the circle
5. an angle whose vertex and a point on each ray lie on the circle
6. an angle whose vertex is the center of a circle and whose rays intersect the circle

Notes 10.7—Investigating the Circumference to Diameter Ratio

MATH CONTENT

- Circles, circumference, diameter, ratio

MATERIALS

- Each group will need a pair of scissors, string, ruler, and two circular objects to measure.

CONNECTIONS

- This activity revisits the ideas investigated in Activity 7.12. If your students have already done Activity 7.12, tie these ideas back to their investigation in 7.12.

TIMETABLE

- 20 minutes for activity
- 10 minutes for class discussion

ACTIVITY DISCUSSION

Encourage each group member to take a role in the investigation. Have students think about how the table could be drawn for maximum benefit and clarity of results. During the discussion of the class results, ask students to explain why they think the ratio holds.

ACTIVITY SOLUTIONS

Part 1: Students should find that C/D is approximately 3.
Part 2: $C/D = \pi$; $C = \pi D$; $C = 2\pi r$

Notes 10.8—Investigating the Area of a Circle

MATH CONTENT

- Circles, area, parallelograms

MATERIALS

- Each person will need a compass, and a piece of construction paper larger than 8.5" x 11". Each group needs tape or glue.

TIMETABLE

- 20 minutes for activity
- 10 minutes for class discussion

ACTIVITY DISCUSSION

Students should recall or use the formula for the area of rectangle. Be sure they spend at least 10 minutes discussing/solving the application problems. The discussion should bring out the plausibility of the area of a circle.

ACTIVITY SOLUTIONS

Part 1
1. a rectangle
2. yes
3. the dimensions of the parallelogram are: height = r and base = πr
   since the circumference of the circle is 2πr and the edge of the circle is split between the opposite sides of the parallelogram, the base is one-half of the circumference

Part 2
1. 11,304 square kilometers; area is in square units
2. area of 1st section is: 9π square cm
   area of 2nd section is: 36π square cm
   so the second section is 4 times stronger than the first

Notes 10.9—Surface Area and Volume of Rectangular Prisms

MATH CONTENT

- Rectangular prisms, cubes, polyhedron, surface area, volume

MATERIALS

- 20 cube blocks per group

TIMETABLE

- 15 minutes for activity
- 5-10 minutes for class discussion

ACTIVITY DISCUSSION

Encourage students to use what they know about 2-dimensional measurements and extend them to 3-dimensional measurements.

ACTIVITY SOLUTIONS

1. a. answers will vary; some possibilities are: box, child's block
   b. has six faces, all faces are congruent squares, adjacent faces are perpendicular, opposite faces are parallel, all edges are congruent, all angles are 90°
   c. a cube is a polyhedron with all its faces congruent squares
   d. 1 cm^3
2. each interior angle of a rectangle is 90°; if four 90° angles meet at a vertex, they form either a plane or angle; if two 90° angles meet, they form an angle; only when 3 90° meet can they form a semi-closed object; so if three 90° angles meet at each of four vertices, this means there will be six faces
3. form a rectangular prism with a layer of blocks that has dimensions x by y. Then stack z layers of this x by y prism on top of each other. Then each layer has xy blocks and there are z layers so this means xy + xy + . . . + xy where xy is added z times. This repeated addition is the same as multiplying xyz.
4. $S = 2xy + 2yz + 2xz$
5. $S = 2s^2 + 2s^2 + 2s^2 = 6s^2$

Notes 10.10—Drawing Rectangular Prisms

MATH CONTENT

- Rectangular prisms

TIMETABLE

- 15 minutes for activity
- 5-10 minutes for class discussion

ACTIVITY DISCUSSION

Encourage students to talk with other members of their groups about the drawing process as they are drawing.

ACTIVITY SOLUTIONS

1. a. i. below and left of
      ii. above and right of
      iii. above and in front of
      iv. below and in front of
2. below and right of
3. a. no
   b. lower, front corner

Notes 10.11—Exploring the Surface Area of Cones

MATH CONTENT

- Cones, surface area, the approximate nature of all measurement

TIMETABLE

- 15 minutes for activity
- 5-10 minutes for class discussion

ACTIVITY DISCUSSION

When introducing this activity, it will be helpful to draw a picture of a cone and a cone sliced by a plan, labeling the altitude, radius and slant height. As a class discuss the following ideas that will be used in this activity: (a) $C = 2\pi r$, (b) $a^2 + b^2 = c^2$, and (c) the ratio of the removed part of the circumference to the circumference of the circle is equal to the ratio of the central angle of the sector to 360°. For example, ask the students "Suppose we remove 1/4 of a circle, what happens to the circumference?" You should <u>not</u> give the formulas for surface area of a cone. The questions in this activity can be answered by using the above information.

This activity focuses on the changing dimensions of the model as the paper cone is curled up and opened. Encourage each student to visualize how the radius and height change. Note that only the lateral area of the cone is formed by the paper. The circular base is located by, but not actually part of, the paper model.

ACTIVITY SOLUTIONS

1. decrease
2. remain fixed at 8 cm
3. 8 cm
4. 8 cm
5. 0 cm
6. 8 cm
7. a. increases   b. increases
8. yes   b. no, the total area approaches twice the area of the original 8 cm circle
9. the radius first increases and then decreases

Notes 10.12—Investigating the Volumes of Cylinders and Cones

MATH CONTENT

- Cylinders, cones, volume, the approximate nature of all measurement, limit

MATERIALS

- Each group will need (a) a different sized clean, empty can (coffee can, juice can, etc.), (b) a manila folder, (c) scissors and tape, (d) enough rice to fill can, and (e) paper clip.

TIMETABLE

- 45 minutes for activity
- 15 minutes for class discussion

ACTIVITY DISCUSSION

The first part of the activity has students investigate the relationship between the volume of a cone and the volume of a cylinder with the same base and height.

The second part of the activity focuses on the changing dimensions of the model as the paper cone is curled up and opened. Encourage each student to visualize how the radius and height change. Note that only the lateral area of the cone is formed by the paper. The circular base is located by, but not actually part of, the paper model. Be sure that each student moves the model through all possible positions in studying the changing volume, as it first will increase but then begin to decrease. This is most obvious when one notes the extreme positions of the cone. Encourage students to make a generalization concerning the radius and height change and the volume of the cone.

Have students compare the positions they chose for maximum volume with the choices of others in the class. The students should make a frequency distribution of the numbers choosing the various lettered positions. The model has been marked so that the diameters for the lettered positions are in centimeters and the radii in 0.5 centimeters. Be sure the heights are also recorded in 0.5 centimeters so that the volume will be in cubic centimeters. Discuss how the idea of multiple representations is used here to visualize the relationships in a different way (through graphing).

Students should plot enough points on the graph that some trend in the changing volume can be observed. This will help give a better collective estimate of the maximum position. The best choice of letters for the maximum volume occurs at C, radius 6.5 centimeters. This is certain to surprise most students. This is a good time to discuss the idea of limit and when a limit is reached for the maximum volume and why.

ACTIVITY SOLUTIONS

Comparing the Volume of a Cylinder and a Cone

Volume of a cylinder: $\pi r^2 h$

Volume of a cone: $(1/3) \pi r^2 h$

Maximizing the Volume of a Cone
The correct values for each letter can be found in the table below.

Radius (cm)	Height (cm)	Volume (cm^2)
6	5.29	199.49
6.1	5.18	201.69
6.2	5.06	203.51
6.3	4.93	204.93
6.4	4.8	205.89
6.5	4.66	206.34
6.6	4.52	206.23
6.7	4.37	205.5
6.8	4.21	204.07
6.9	4.05	201.84
7	3.87	198.73

Extension
To verify the students' results, you might want to fill the variously shaped cones with rice and compare their volumes by that method. The exact maximum volume possible for a cone with a slant height of 8 cm can be found using calculus techniques. The greatest volume is 206.37 cubic cm, and it occurs at a radius of 6.53 cm.

Notes 10.13—Geoboard Battleship: Exploring Coordinate Geometry

MATH CONTENT

- Coordinate geometry

MATERIALS

- 2 geoboards and rubber bands for each group

TIMETABLE

- 20 minutes for activity
- 10 minutes for class discussion

ACTIVITY DISCUSSION

While this activity deals with 2-dimensional coordinates, there is a fair amount of careful reasoning skills that students will need to answer the questions. For example, it is tempting, in #2, to conclude that there are 16 possible locations for the gunboat. However, the gunboat cannot be placed with a vertex at (3, 3) because the larger destroyer needs that peg, regardless of where it is placed.

Counting the number of locations where the various ships can be placed is very similar to the kind of reasoning that can be used to solve the classic problem, "How many squares are on a checkerboard?", as well as the more challenging problem, "How many rectangles are on a checkerboard?"

Question #6 is, like #7, a best-case situation. Two guesses would be sufficient to win the game, but only if the center of the destroyer were located at (3, 2) or (4, 3), or (3, 4) or (2, 3), and only if team B makes two lucky guesses. It is often helpful, however, to get comfortable with a situation by considering extreme cases. Thus, after discussing the best-case scenario of #6, it might be helpful to also consider a worst-case scenario for team B.

In question #7, the situation changes quite a bit, just by adding another row and column. Now, there are far fewer limitations as far as placing ships is concerned. (However, there is still one location where one of the ships cannot be placed.)

Finally, it should be pointed out that many students may be somewhat familiar with this game, having played the board game "Battleship" (which was originally adapted from a pencil-and-paper game). It may be worth exploring, in light of this activity, some strategies that might be used in playing the board game.

Notes 10.14 - 10.16—Transformations
Investigating Translations, Rotations & Reflections
using the *Geometer's Sketchpad*™

MATH CONTENT

- Isometries—translations, rotations, reflections

MATERIALS

- *Geometer's Sketchpad*™ software

TIMETABLE

- 60 minutes for activities
- 10 minutes for class discussion

ACTIVITY DISCUSSION

This is an optional activity since it requires students to use *Geometer's Sketchpad*™ software. This activity will engage students in exploring isometries. We suggest that students work in pairs for the *Sketchpad*™ investigations. Students should have a chance to be both investigator and observer. It is important they understand the investigation so an overview at the beginning should be provided. You may want to have the *Sketchpad*™ Quick Reference pages available if needed for clarification.

Monitor the timing of each activity. Page 350 may take about 30 minutes but the others can be completed in 15 to 20 minutes. Allow students time to finish all three before focusing discussion of the property of isometries: congruence is preserved. Also discuss orientations of the translated images of each isometry.

ACTIVITY SOLUTIONS

For all three investigations, students should discover that length and distance are preserved by isometries (congruence).

Notes 10.17—Tessellations: One Definition

MATH CONTENT

- Angle measurement, angle addition, tessellations, tilings

MATERIALS

- Pattern blocks for each group
- Have multiple copies of the cut out shapes on page 358 for each group

CONNECTIONS

- Exercises and More Problems: #63-64

TIMETABLE

- 60 minutes for activities
- 10 minutes for class discussion

ACTIVITY DISCUSSION

When introducing this two-part activity, a brief history of tessellations will provide some motivation and interest for doing the activity. The following historical note is taken from Bezuszka, S., Kenney, M., Silvey, L. (1977). *Tessellations: The geometry of patterns* (p. 1). Palo Alto, CA: Creative Publications, Inc.

> The design of geometric shapes that individually or in combination cover a flat surface without gaps or overlappings has a long history. The Sumerians (about 4000 B.C.) in the Mesopotamian Valley built homes and temples decorated with mosaics in geometric patterns. The materials used in the mosaics were thin slabs of burned clay, called tiles. When colored and glazed, tiles served not only as part of the structure of buildings but also as artistic decorations.
> Later, the Persians showed that they were masters in tile decorations. Similarly, the Moors used congruent, multicolored tiles on the walls and floors of their buildings. Moslem and Islamic tile patterns with striking colors still survive.
> Roman buildings, floors, and pavements were decorated with tiles which the Romans called *tessellae*. The Roman word *tessellae* is the root of our English word *tessellation*.

When students are finding the regular polygons that tessellate the plane, refer them to the table from Activity 9.16. A quick check for which measures are factors of 360 will enable students to make their determinations. This is a great time to talk about decomposition of numbers as a fundamental idea throughout mathematics.

When the students start looking for semi-regular tessellations, help them be systematic. The main idea is that of subtracting the measure of one angle of a particular regular polygon from 360 and then looking for factors of the difference that are also measures of angles. The most common error students are likely to make is that of forgetting that these polygons can be rearranged in several different orders. Since the order is important in a vertex arrangement, it is possible to use the same polygons in different ways to produce various semi-regular tessellations. There are 8 semi-regular tessellations. These arrangements are given below and diagrams (from which overhead transparencies can be made) for each of these arrangements are included here for use *after* students have found the arrangements.

Give students plenty of opportunities to generate conjectures and write generalizations about which shapes will tessellate the plane. Help them to explain to the class as a whole how they made their determinations about which figures will tessellate. One of the big ideas in this activity is that of definitions and how they affect the structure of the topic at hand. In the next activity, students will work with a different definition of tessellation. Hopefully, with your help, they will see that changing the definition of tessellation changes the need to require that vertex figures be regular. This idea of precision in language, especially in definitions, is fundamental in mathematics, and it is crucial that these students begin to understand that. Emphasize this kind of structure during the class discussion.

When they use non-regular figures, some of their shapes may not work. For example, some pentagons will tessellate the plane, but others will not. Students may also need help with the concave quadrilaterals. You many need to have some cardboard examples ready to use on the board. The question is whether every quadrilateral will tessellate the plane. Be prepared with an answer. You might start by looking at the sum of the measures of the angles in a quadrilateral. Is it always 360°, regardless of concavity? What does this imply in regard to the conditions polygons must meet in order to tessellate the plane?

Semi-regular Tessellations

A tessellation of the plane with a combination of two or more kinds of regular polygons arranged so that every vertex point is congruent to every other vertex point is called a *semi-regular tessellation*; that is, the same polygons appear in the same order at each vertex point. Semi-regular tessellations are described by giving, in order, the number of sides of the polygons at a vertex point. The counting usually begins with the polygon that has the smallest number of sides at a vertex point and move (clockwise or counterclockwise) about the vertex point, writing down the number of sides of the polygons involved.

Regular Tessellations (using regular polygons)
1. 3.3.3.3.3.3   Six triangles at each vertex point
2. 4.4.4.4   Four squares at each vertex point
3. 6.6.6   Three hexagons at each vertex point

Semi-regular Tessellations (using regular polygons)
1. 3.3.3.3.6   Four triangles and a hexagon at each vertex point
2. 3.3.3.4.4   Three triangles and two squares at each vertex point
3. 3.4.6.4   Triangle, square, hexagon, square at each vertex point
4. 4.8.8   Square and two octagons at each vertex point
5. 3.6.3.6   Triangle, hexagon, triangle, hexagon at each vertex point
6. 3.3.4.3.4   Two triangles, square, triangle, square at each vertex point
7. 3.12.12   Triangle, and two dodecagons at each vertex point
8. 4.6.12   Square, hexagon, dodecagon at each vertex point

Extension

You may want to discuss this with your class. Suppose we had used the following different definition of a regular tessellation: A tessellation is regular if it is composed entirely of regular polygons whose vertex figures are also regular polygons. (A vertex figure is the polygon formed by connecting the midpoints of all the sides that meet at any one particular vertex.) Using this new definition, do we get any new tessellations? Is it possible to have a regular tessellation where the vertex figures are not regular polygons? If you say yes, demonstrate your tessellation. If you say no, analyze and discuss this new definition of regular tessellation. Does it have any extraneous conditions in it? Does it say too much or too little?

ACTIVITY SOLUTIONS

1. tiling, tessellation, tiling, tessellation
3. equilateral triangle, square, regular hexagon (only regular figures whose angle measures are factors of 360)

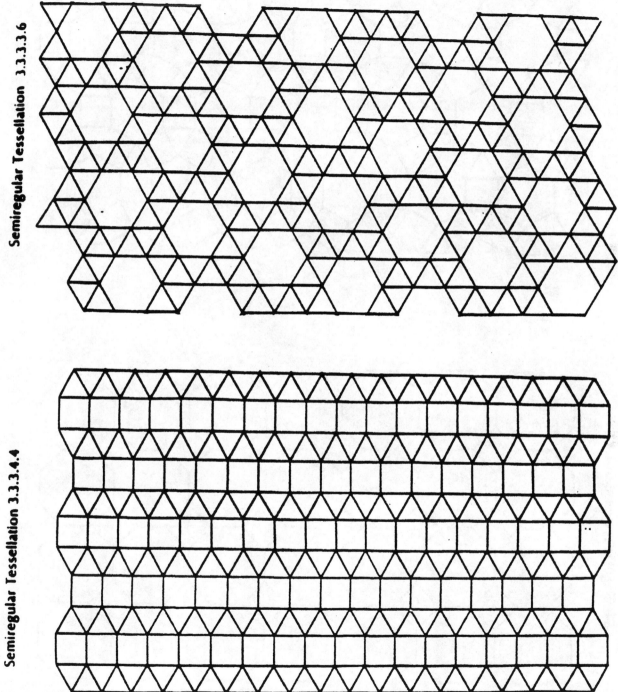

Semiregular Tessellation 3.3.3.3.6

Semiregular Tessellation 3.3.3.4.4

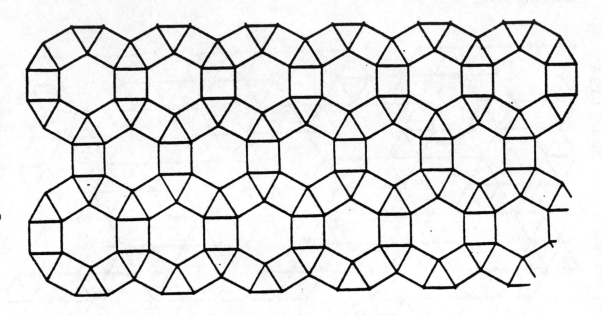

Semiregular Tessellation 3.4.6.4

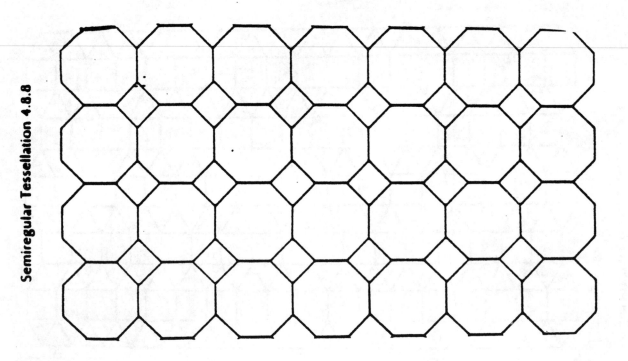

Semiregular Tessellation 4.8.8

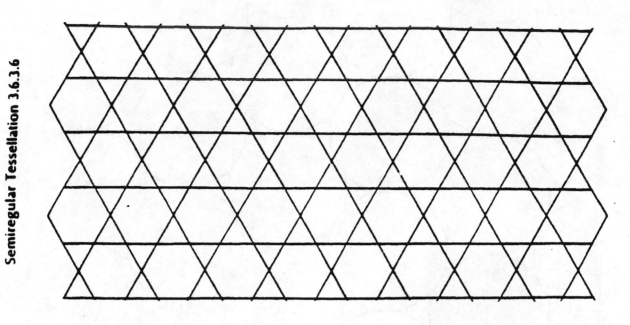

Semiregular Tessellation 3.6.3.6

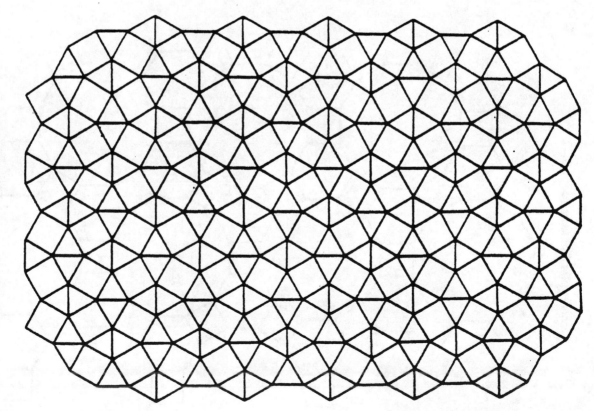

Semiregular Tessellation 3.3.4.3.4

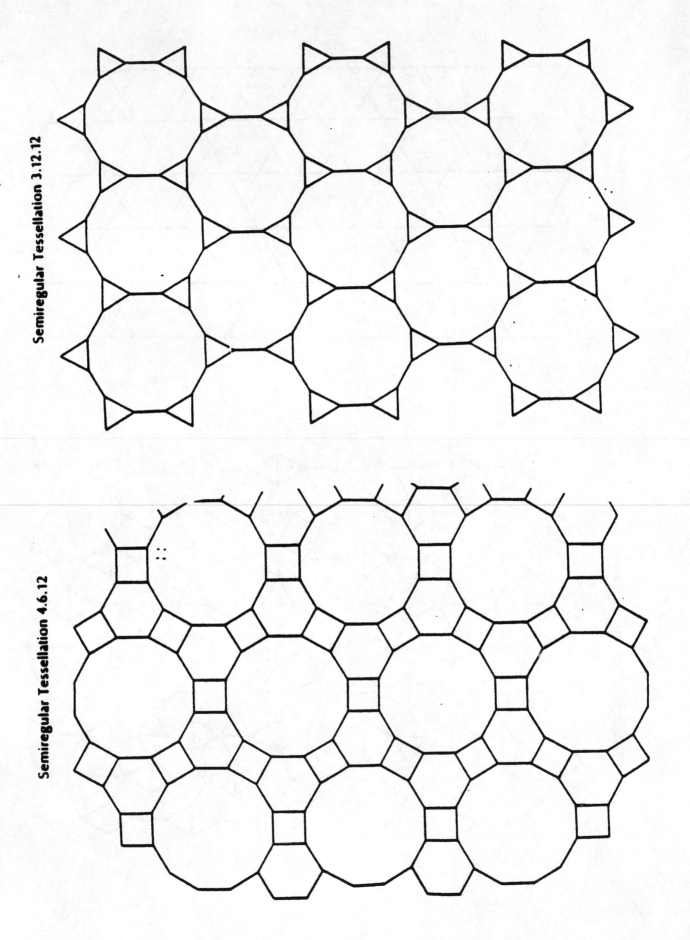

Semiregular Tessellation 3.12.12

Semiregular Tessellation 4.6.12

Notes 10.18—Tessellations: Another Definition

MATH CONTENT

- Angle measurement, angle addition, tessellations, tilings, dual of a tessellation

MATERIALS

- Compass, straightedge, scissors

CONNECTIONS

- This activity follows up on Activity 10.17 and should only be done after 10.17 has been completed.

TIMETABLE

- 45 minutes for activities
- 15 minutes for class discussion

ACTIVITY DISCUSSION

The whole reason for talking about tessellations in this second activity is to take advantage of the changes in the structure of this particular topic in mathematics caused by changing the definition of tessellation. If we require tessellations to be composed so that corners meet at corners (i.e., there is no alternation such as one might see in a brick wall), then the definition of regular tessellation listed below has extraneous information in it.

If, on the other hand, we allow any tiling to be a tessellation, then the definition of regular tessellation must change. The following are some examples of possibilities for new definitions.

<u>Definition</u>: A *tessellation* of the plane is an arrangement of polygonal regions such that the polygonal regions have only their sides in common and all points of the plane are covered by some polygonal region. (Note: This definition allows for alternating rows such as that found in brick work.)

<u>Definition</u>: A tessellation is a *regular tessellation* if it is constructed entirely of regular polygons and all the vertex figures are also regular polygons.

<u>Definition</u>: The *dual of a tessellation* is the tessellation obtained by connecting the centers of the polygons in the original tessellation that share a common side. For example, the dual of the tessellation of equilateral triangles is the tessellation of regular hexagons (shown below).

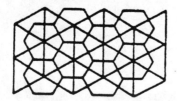

Allow students plenty of time for exploration to find a new definition. Many students will need help in verifying whether or not the old definition still works. Help them to start drawing examples and counterexamples. Write the student-generated definitions of the board, then modify them as the students refine their ideas. Come up with a concrete (written) product to show how we can write precise definitions. Note: It may be difficult for students to grasp the significance of changing definitions.

Help students draw the dual of several tessellations. Try to find some generalizations about the dual of a tessellation. Emphasize the mathematical structure involved in this activity and how it changes depending upon the definition used.

Solutions to Exercises & More Problems

Chapter 1

1. various solutions are possible; one possibility is: 8, 16, 32; another possibility is 7, 11, 16

2. B, B, A

3. 116, 159, 209

4. 143, 219, 318

5. 16, 19, 22

6. answers will vary

7. answers will vary

8. understanding the problem, making a plan, implementing the plan, looking back

9. a. The following table shows one way in which Rebekah could get 6 cups and 1 cup of water. It lists the amount of water at each step in each of the cups. Only one transfer has been made at each step. Remember, since it is water that is needed Rebekah could afford to throw away the unused quantities of water.

5 cup vessel	8 cup vessel
0	8
5 (throw away)	3
3	0
3	8
5 (throw away)	6 --> Amount needed for the recipe

   b. 5   1

   c. Once Rebekah gets 1 cup of water, she can get any other quantity (in whole cups), by storing the 1 cup in another vessel, and adding on any more cups of water.

10. In this case, there are only three vessels that can be used, and the cider cannot be thrown away. So the 4- gallon amounts must be got by manipulating the amounts within the containers. The following table shows the amounts of cider at each step in the three vessels. Only one transfer has been made at each step.

8-gallon barrel	5-gallon barrel	3-gallon barrel
8	0	0
3	5	0
3	2	3
6	2	0
1	5	2
1	4	3
4	4	0

11. a. You can get all those and only those values that are sums or multiples of 5 and 8; that is all those values that are of the form 8x + 5y, where x and y are non-negative whole numbers. The numbers 7, 14 and 17 cannot be obtained. The following combinations show some possible amounts.
$$18 = 8 \cdot 1 + 5 \cdot 2$$
$$31 = 8 \cdot 2 + 5 \cdot 3$$
$$41 = 8 \cdot 2 + 5 \cdot 5$$
$$43 = 8 \cdot 1 + 5 \cdot 7$$
$$52 = 8 \cdot 4 + 5 \cdot 4.$$
In fact, every number greater than 27 can be obtained.

　　b. The numbers 1, 2, 3, 4, 6, 7, 9, 11, 12, 14, 17, 19, and 27 cannot be obtained.

12. answers will vary

13. a. $23.01.
　　b. At the end of December; at the end of March the following year.

14. Two weighings.
Take six coins, and place three on each side of the balance scale.
Case I: If these are equal, then one of the two remaining coins is heavier. By placing one on each side of the balance, you can determine the heavier one.
Case II: In the first weighing, one side is heavier than the other. From the heavier side, take two coins, and place one on each side. The heavier side has the heavier coin. If they are equal, then the remaining coin is heavier.
In either case, you can determine the result with two weighings.

15. 9 minutes.
Adam can put the first two waffles into the griddle, and let the first side of both cook—this takes three minutes. He then flips over one waffle, but removes the second one from the griddle, and puts in the third one. At the end of end of another 3 minutes, both the sides of the first waffle, and one side each of the second and the third waffles are done. So he removes the first waffle and lets the second side of both the second and third waffles cook for another 3 minutes. Thus, total time taken is 3 + 3 + 3 = 9 minutes.

16. 13 hours. Twelve hours for the first 12 feet, and 1 hour for the last three feet—at this point the spider has already reached the top.

17. The first number is larger. It can be explained by using the distributive property, and the formula for the sum of the first n numbers.

18. Sara has 8 horses (and 19 hens).
　　　　Solving the problem algebraically, we get:
　　　　x + y = 27
　　　　2x + 4y = 70, where x and y represent the number of hens and horses respectively.
　　　　Solving the equations simultaneously, we get y = 8, and x = 19.
Other ways of solving the problem may include making a table with possible values of each kind of animal, or drawing out a picture as follows:
Here, each animal is given two legs and the extra legs are then distributed in pairs until all 70 legs are exhausted.

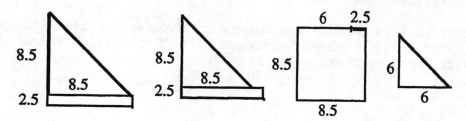

19. Pull out a ball from the box marked "Red and White Balls." This should give us the solution. For example, if the ball you extract is white, then this box should be marked "White Balls," the one marked "White Balls" should be marked "Red Balls" and the one marked "Red Balls" should read "Red and White Balls."

20. First fold the width of the paper over the length. This leaves 2.5 in on the longer side. Subtract the 2.5 in from the width of the paper to get 6 in. Now fold the paper diagonally to get the square.

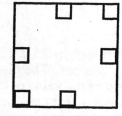

21. The order is: Tom - 156 lbs., Harry - 152 lbs., Max - 138 lbs., John - 135 lbs., Eric - 130 lbs., and Kevin - 120 lbs.

22. a. Stratford –> Hastings –> Blissville
    b. Morgantown –> Stratford –> Temple –> Mapletown
    c. See d. below.
    d. Pinesville –> Williamsburg –> Stratford –> Hastings –> Blissville –> Oakwood
    e. Hastings –> Blissville –> Pinesville –> Williamsburg
    f. Mapletown –> Williamsburg –> Stratford –> Brackport
    g. Stratford –> Hastings –> Blissville –> Pinesville
    h. Not possible.
    i. Pinesville –> Williamsburg –> Stratford –> Temple –> Mapletown
    j. Temple –> Mapletown –> Williamsburg –> Stratford –> Hastings

23. The plants could be arranged as follows:

24. A sketch of the paths will help you to deduce the answers.

25. 28th day

26. 1024 pages

27. Sara—$39, Cathy—$21, Tina—$12

28. 2

29. 1

30. 307

31. first move should be to the middle peg

32. first move should be to right peg

33. if you have an even number of disks, the first move should be to the peg which is not the target peg; if you have an odd number of disks, the first move should be to the target peg

34. One such number is 23421314.

35. You always get a number of the form nnnnnn, where n is the original number. Thus, with 3 you get 333333, and with 5, 555555. This happens because 273 • 407 = 111111. You could factor 111111 differently to get other numbers in place of 273 and 407.

36. a. 64 cubes
    b. i.   none
       ii. 8 cubes
       iii. 24 cubes
       iv. 24 cubes
       v.   8 cubes

Chapter 2

1.
72	▼ < ▼▼	⋔⋔⋔⋔ II	≡	LXXII
1,273	<< ▼ < ▼▼▼	𝄑 ⁊⁊⋔⋔⋔⋔ ⋂⋂ III	≡	MCCLXXIII
1,813	<<< < ▼▼▼	𝄑 ⁊⁊⁊⁊⁊⁊⁊⋂ III	≡	MDCCCXIII
1,965	<<< ▼▼ <<<< ▼▼▼▼▼	𝄑 ⁊⁊⁊⁊⁊⁊⁊⁊⁊⋂⋂⋔⋔⋔ IIIII	≡	MCMLXV
121	▼▼ ▼	⁊⋂⋂ I	•	CXXI
231	▼▼▼ <<<<< ▼	⁊⁊⋂⋂⋔ I	≐	CCXXXI

2. 154; 341

3. a. A numeration system is said to be a place value system if the value of each digit in a number in the system is determined by its position in the number. The place value of a digit is a description of its position in a given number that determines the value of the digit. In the given number, 2 represents 200, 5 represents 50, 4 represents 4, 7 represents 7/10 and 1 represents 1/100.

   b. A numeration system is said to be multiplicative if each symbol in a number in that system represents a different multiple of the face value of that symbol. In the given number, the 2 represents the multiple $2 \cdot 10^2$, the 5 represents $5 \cdot 10^1$, the 4 represents the $4 \cdot 1$, the 7 represents $7 \cdot 10^{-1}$, and the 1 represents $1 \cdot 10^{-2}$.

   c. A numeration system is said to be additive if the value of the set of symbols representing a number is the sum of the values of the individual symbols. In the given number, the value of the number is equal to $200 + 50 + 4 + .7 + .01$.

   d. A numeration system is a unique representation system if each numeral refers to one and only one number, since there is only one number that is represented by 254.71.

4. hundreds; thousands; units (or ones)

5. answers will be of the form 53x0, where x represents any digit but could also have digits in the places higher than thousands

6. a. 7 is in the 8^2 place;

   b. answer will be in the form 3xx, where x represents any digit but could also have digits in the places higher than 7^2

   c. $3 \cdot 10^5 + 5 \cdot 10^4 + 6 \cdot 10^3 + 4 \cdot 10^2 + 7 \cdot 10^1 + 5 \cdot 10^0$

     $1 \cdot 2^6 + 1 \cdot 2^5 + 0 \cdot 2^4 + 1 \cdot 2^3 + 0 \cdot 2^2 + 0 \cdot 2^1 + 1 \cdot 2^0$

     $5 \cdot 12^4 + 10 \cdot 12^3 + 3 \cdot 12^2 + 9 \cdot 12^1 + 0 \cdot 12^0$

     $2 \cdot 5^4 + 1 \cdot 5^3 + 3 \cdot 5^2 + 2 \cdot 5^1 + 2 \cdot 5^0$

7. a. 5,546   b. 206   c. 371   d. 244,107

8. a. 221112_{three} b. 3840_{eleven} c. 1301_{five}

9. a. x = five   b. x = seven

10. f

11. Starting with 20_{four} means you have 2 longs. Trade in one long for 4 units. Now you have 1 long and 4 units. Removing 1 long and 3 units leaves you with one unit.

12. Starting with 1200_{four} means you have 1 cube and 2 flats. Trade in one flat for 4 longs. Then trade in 1 long for 4 units. Now you have 1 cube, 1 flat, 3 longs, and 4 units. Remove 3 longs and 3 units and you are left with 1 cube, 1 flat and 1 unit.

13. base three: 1 cube, 2 longs, 2 units; base six: 5 longs, 5 units

14. 3 quarters, 2 nickels, and 2 pennies

15. $3 \cdot 5^2 + 2 \cdot 5^1 + 4 \cdot 5^0 + 1 \cdot 5^{-1} + 2 \cdot 5^{-2} + 2 \cdot 5^{-3}$

16. $a \cdot n^3 + b \cdot n^2 + c \cdot n^1 + d \cdot n^0 + e \cdot n^{-1} + f \cdot n^{-2} + g \cdot n^{-3}$

17. a. i. 326, 057   ii. 1,802,036

   b. i.   ii.

18.

	11	13	21
20	31	33	101
23	100	102	110
111	122	130	132

19.

	31	41	43
21	52	102	104
34	105	115	121
51	122	132	134

20. $900E000T_{twelve}$

21. $7006000T_{eleven}$

22. a. $1696T7_{eleven}$ b. 10110010_{two} c. 1741_{eight}
    d. 1813_{twelve} e. 223021_{four} f. 34462_{seven}

23. 3 gal 2 qts 1 cup; base 4

24. 14 hrs 18 min 16 sec; base 60

25. 2 yd 2 ft 8 in; no base

26. 2 km 998 m 993 mm; base 1000

27. trade and regroup as needed

28. 14 yd 8 in

29. 1 yd 3.5 in

30. 15 Tbsp 2 tsp

31. 1 qt 15 Tbsp

32. look for largest power of unit, subtract that amount, repeat same method until finished

33. even though these situations do not have one consistent base, these conversions are similar to converting a number from one base to another because of the method of looking for the largest power of a unit (base), subtracting that amount, and repeating this process

34. 1 hr 25 min 44 sec

35. Using an organized list and looking for a pattern is one way to find the solution to the Sultan problem. The place of the first wife to receive a ring in the nth round is 3^{n-2} more than the place of the first wife to receive a ring in the (n -1)st round, where n ≥ 2. Thus, the generalized solution is

$1 + \sum 3^k$, where k = 0 to n - 2.

The answer is 9842 wives. This number is $111111112_{base\ three}$. Writing the number in base three will help you better understand the problem and where the idea of multiples of three fits in.

36. Yes, a system could be multiplicative but not have a base if each symbol is multiplied by numbers other than different powers of the same number.

37. Draw out one coin from the box labeled 35¢. If it is a dime, then the box should be labeled 20¢, and if it is a quarter, then it should be labeled 50¢. Given that all the three boxes are labeled incorrectly, it is now easy to work out the other labels. (This problem is similar to #19 in Chapter 1.)

38. a. fiefotfot, foefotfot, fumfotfot, fotfotfot, feefotfotfot, fiefotfotfot, foefotfotfot, fumfotfotfot, fotfotfotfot

    b. base 2—even number has 0 in units, odd has 1 in units
        base 3—no characterization
        base 4—even number has 0 or 2 in units, odd has 1 or 3
        base 5—no characterization
        fee, fie, foe, fum—no characterization

39. 222222 is the largest six-digit base three numeral since if you add 1, you would have 1000000 (a seven-digit numeral)

40. a. base 26   b. 675

41. They were using base 7, while the adventurer was using base 10.

42. a. 12   b. 9   c. 59
    d. 117   e. 18   f. 48

43. four weights—1, 2, 4, and 8 grams; six weights—1, 2, 4, 8, 16, and 32 grams; 63 grams

44. four weights—1, 2, 4, and 8 pounds; every weight (1 - 15 pounds) can be measured by using some combination of these four weights

45. 8 is the larger number; 5 is the larger numeral

46. a. Children have to understand place value in order to realize that 13 is different from 31 and since this is a difficult concept, it is not surprising that some children have trouble with reversals
    b. The subtractive characteristic of the Roman numeral system might have given ancient Roman children difficulties since IXC could be 91 or 89. Egyptian children might have had difficulties since for large numbers, there were many symbols to write. Most of the symbols required a fair amount of fine motor skills and would have been difficult for young children.

47. a. 6 weights—1, 2, 4, 8, 16, and 32 ozs.
    b. 1 weight—1 oz.
    c. 4 weights—1, 3, 9, 27 ozs.
    d. base two, base three
    e. both use base two system

Chapter 3

1. a. $(3 + 4) + 8 = 3 + (4 + 8)$
   b. $7 \cdot 5 = 5 \cdot 7$
   c. $4 + 0 = 4$
   d. $3 \cdot 1/3 = 1$

2. a. No, @ is not commutative; 5 @ 3 = 15 - 6 = 9 but 3 @ 5 = 9 - 10 = -1.
   b. No, @ is not associative; (5 @ 3) @ 2 = 9 @ 2 = 27 - 4 = 23, but 5 @ (3 @ 2) = 5 @ (9 - 4) = 5 @ 5 = 15 - 10 = 5.
   c. No, the set of whole numbers is not closed under @ since 3 @ 5 = -1.
   d. No, x @ x = 3x - 2x = x, so in some sense every number is its own identity, but when a set has an identity element under an operation, the identity is supposed to be the same for all numbers in the set.

3. a. Yes, a is the additive identity because a added to any element will equal that element.
    b. Yes, order in adding does not change the result; the table is symmetric.
    c. Yes, b has c for an inverse since b + c = a.

4. a. No, a @ b = c, and c is not in {a, b}.
    b. Yes, any two elements under @ equal an element of {a, b, c}.
    c. No, a @ c = a, c @ a = c and b @ b = b.
    d. No, a @ c = a but c @ a = c.
    e. No, elements cannot have inverses if there is no identity.

5. 4 ÷ (8 - 4) ≠ (4 ÷ 8) - (4 ÷ 4) because 1 ≠ -1/2.

6. One possible way for each statement is shown below.
    a. (3 + 9) – (4 + 2) = 4
    b. 3 + 9 – 4 + 2 = 10 (No parentheses needed)
    c. 7 • (2 + 5) = 49
    d. (7 + 6) – (4 • 2) = 5
    e. 3 • (5 + 2) = 21

7. word problems will be similar to those in Activity 3.3

8. word problems will be similar to those in Activity 3.3

9. b, g, h, b, a

10. a. integer—positive   b. integer—negative   c. not integer
    d. integer—neither   e. not integer   f. integer—positive
    g. not integer   h. integer—positive

11. illustrations will be similar to those in Activity 3.4

12. a.
```
        2   1
        6   3   4
        1   5   8₂
           4₃   2
       3₂  9₂   2
     +  5   1   0
     ─────────────
       1  7   3   6
```
    b.
```
          2   2
          6   4   5
              3   4
        3₁  7₆  9₈
            4₆  8₆
      +   2   5   2
      ─────────────
        1   3   5   8
```

13. a.
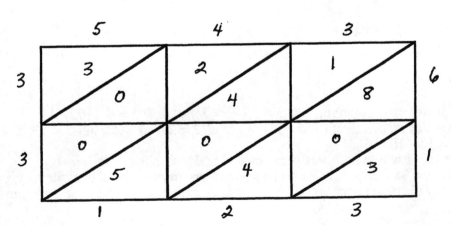

    The product is 33,123.

b.

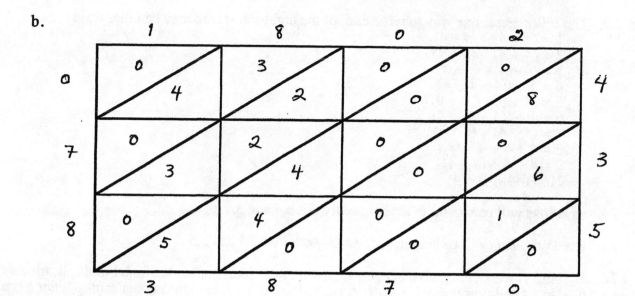

The product is 783,870.

14. a. 22, 23, 24, 25, 30
    b. 21.50, 21.75, 22, 23, 24, 25, 30 (answer may vary)
    c. 26.80, 26.90, 27, 28, 29, 30

15. a.
$$
\begin{array}{cccc}
6 & {}^{\prime}3 & {}^{\prime}1 \\
-\ {}^{3}\!\!\not{2} & {}^{9}\!\!\not{8} & 7 \\
\hline
3 & 4 & 4
\end{array}
$$

    b.
$$
\begin{array}{cccc}
2 & {}^{\prime}4 & {}^{\prime}2 & {}^{\prime}3 \\
-\ {}^{2}\!\!\not{1} & {}^{7}\!\!\not{6} & {}^{6}\!\!\not{5} & 7 \\
\hline
& 7 & 6 & 6
\end{array}
$$

16. a.
13	•	59
~~6~~	•	~~118~~
3	•	236
1	•	472

   $13 • 59 = 59 + 236 + 472$
   $\qquad = 767$

   b.
23	•	62
11	•	124
5	•	248
~~2~~	•	~~496~~
1	•	992

   $23 • 62 = 62 + 124 + 248 + 992$
   $\qquad = 1426$

17. △ + ▭ ○

18. △○ + ▭ ◇

19. △ ▭ ÷ ○

20. ◇ − △ ○

21. ○ − ▭ + ◇

22. (○ + ◇ ▭) ÷ △

23. The following is one way to write each of the numbers. There may be other ways.
$$1 = (4 \div 4) + (4 - 4)$$
$$2 = (4 \div 4) + (4 \div 4)$$
$$3 = (4 + 4 + 4) \div 4$$
$$4 = 4 + ((4 - 4) \cdot 4)$$
$$5 = (4 + (4 \cdot 4)) \div 4$$
$$6 = 4 + ((4 + 4) \div 4)$$
$$7 = (4 + 4) - (4 \div 4)$$
$$8 = 4 + 4 + 4 - 4$$
$$9 = 4 + 4 + (4 \div 4)$$
$$10 = (44 - 4) \div 4$$

24. equations will be similar to those in Activities 3.4 and 3.5

25. word problems will be similar to those in Activities 3.4 and 3.5

26. a. No. The set of negative integers is closed under addition, but not under multiplication.
    b. No. The set of multiples of four, {4, 8, 16, 24, . . . }, is closed under multiplication but not under addition.

27. The set must be {1, 2, 3, 4, . . . } = Natural numbers. Since the set is closed under addition and 1 is in the set, then $1 + 1 = 2$ is in the set. Then $2 + 1 = 3$ is in the set, and so on.

28. $a - b = a + -b = -b + a$ demonstrates the commutative property for addition. However, if subtraction was commutative that would mean that $a - b = b - a$ or $a + -b = b + -a$, which is not true.

29. $-x$ does not mean that $-x$ is negative; it simply means the opposite of x. If $x < 0$, then $|x| = -x$.

30. a. true   b. true   c. false   d. true
    e. false   f. false   g. true

31. a.
```
    ²2  ³¹  
     2  3  4
   1 ⁵³ ⁸¹
     ⁴¹ 2
   ⁸² 0  2
 + ⁵¹ 1  0
 ─────────────
   2  1  2  5_six
```
b.
```
    ³1 ²⁴₀ 5
        3 ⁴³
   ⁸₁ 2  1
      ⁴³ 0
 + 1 ⁵₂ ²₀
 ─────────────
 1  2  2  0_six
```

32. a.

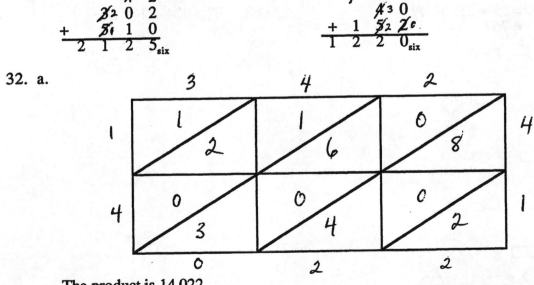

The product is 14,022.

b.

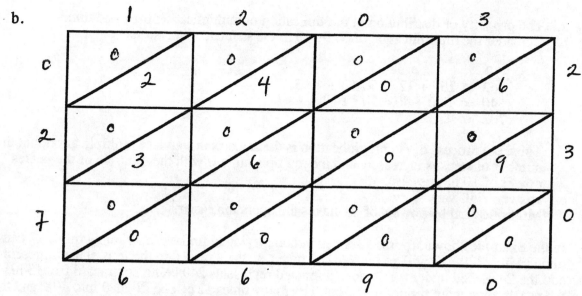

The product is 276,690.

33.
```
            -3
         -3   0
      -2  -1   1
    3  -5   4  -3
  5  -2  -3   7  -10
```

34.
```
               43,200
           -180     -240
         -15   12    -20
       5    3     4    -5
```

35. 26 floors.
The answer can be found as follows: 4 + 10 − 6 + 15 − 3 + 2 + 4 = 26.

36. There are 60 different ways of filling up the posts. Students may draw a tree diagram or draw up lists or just multiply as 5 • 4 • 3 = 60.

37. a. No, if 7 is removed, the set will not be closed any more under addition (e.g., 4 + 3 = 7 does not belong to the set).
    b. If 7 is removed, the set will still remain closed under multiplication since the only way to have a product of 7 is to multiply 7 and 1.
    c. If 6 is removed from the set, the set will lose the property of closure under both addition and multiplication, since 2 • 3 = 6.

38. a. commutative property for addition
    b. the set of whole numbers is closed under multiplication
    c. commutative property for multiplication
    d. 0 is the additive identity
    e. 1/3 is the multiplicative inverse of 3
    f. commutative property for multiplication, associative property for multiplication
    g. commutative property for addition
    h. -5 is the additive inverse of 5

39. a. The property of distribution of multiplication of multiplication over addition.
    b. Consider the multiplication of 54 by 13 in the standard algorithm.

$$\begin{array}{r} 54 \\ \times\ \underline{13} \\ 162 \\ \underline{540} \\ 702 \end{array}$$

$162 = 150 + 12 = 50 \cdot 3 + 4 \cdot 3$
$540 = 500 + 40 = 50 \cdot 10 + 4 \cdot 10$

Thus, the process of the multiplication is the same as in standard multiplication, but the number of steps is increased, and the multiplication is with the multiple of the nearest power of 10 in this case.

    c. answers will vary
    d. Multiplication by powers of 10 makes the operation easier.

40. In the example shown, for the first step you are trying to find out how many times 12 can be divided into 320. 12 will go into 320 20 times, so the 2 placed in the tens place represents 20 and the 24 placed under the 34 and subtracted represents 240 being subtracted from 340. In the next step you are trying to find out how many times 12 can be divided into 108, and the 9 in the ones place means that 12 goes into 108 9 times.

41. Her students would find $42 \div 6$ by repeatedly subtracting 6 and counting the number of times they were able to subtract 6 until they reached 0. Since division can be thought of as repeated subtraction, this algorithm works.

42. answers will vary

Chapter 4

1. a. $2 \cdot 3 \cdot 5 \cdot 7$ b. $2^3 \cdot 17$ c. $2 \cdot 3^3$
    d. $2^3 \cdot 5^3$ e. $2^4 \cdot 5^3$

2. a. $2^2 \cdot 7$ b. $2^3 \cdot 3^2$ c. $7 \cdot 13$

3. $110 = 2 \cdot 5 \cdot 11$ $204 = 2 \cdot 2 \cdot 3 \cdot 17$
    start by dividing numbers by since they are both even, then continue dividing by factors until reach prime number

4. a. composite   b. neither   c. prime   d. composite
    e. prime   f. neither   g. neither

5. 7, 29, 43, 57, and 143 are prime. The others are composite.

6. 16, 28, 32, 56, 102, and 118 are even. The others are odd.

7. a. $12/28 = 3/7$; looked for greatest common factor for 12 and 28, which is 4, and then divided the numerator and denominator by 4
    b. $90/105 = 6/7$; wrote prime factorization for each number, looked for greatest common factor, which is 15, and then divided the numerator and denominator by 15
    c. $\dfrac{2 \cdot 5^2 \cdot 11}{3 \cdot 7}$; looked for common factors to divide out of numerator and denominator

8. a. some possibilities are 2, 3, 5, 7, 11
    b. some possibilities are 4, 9, 25, 49, 121
    c. some possibilities are 6, 8, 10, 15, 27

9. 310 has more than 6 factors because its prime factorization is 2 • 5 • 31. Thus, its factors are 1 & 310; 2 & 155; 5 & 62; 10 & 31

10. a. true   b. false   c. true

11. 3 and 7

12. a. yes, because the sum of the digits is divisible by 3
    b. no, because the sum of the digits is not divisible by 3
    c. yes, because the sum of the digits is divisible by 3

13. a. yes, because it meets the requirements for divisibility by 3 <u>and</u> 8
    b. yes, because it meets the requirements for divisibility by 5 <u>and</u> 8
    c. no, because it does not meet the requirements for divisibility by 9
    d. yes, because it meets the requirements for divisibility by 4 and 9

14. answers will vary

15. a. 44   b. 3   c. 16   d. 8

16. a. 21252   b. 78624   c. 163680   d. 348480

17.   0 1 2 3
       1 2 3 0
       2 3 0 1
       3 0 1 2

    a. 1   b. 2   c. 0

18.   0 0 0 0
       0 1 2 3
       0 2 0 2
       0 3 2 1

    a. no, there is no number that you can multiply 2 by to get 1
    b. yes, 3 since 3 • 3 equals 1 (mod 4)

19. a. 1   b. 3   c. 3   d. 2   e. 5   f. 2   g. 4
    h. 7   i. 4   j. 0   k. 4   l. 0   m. 1   n. 3
    o. 6   p. 2

20. a. 2, since $3 + 2 = 0$ (mod 5)
    b. 2, since $4 + 2 = 0$ (mod 6)
    c. 5, since $2 + 5 = 0$ (mod 7)

21. a. 3, since $5 • 3 = 15 = 1$ (mod 7)
    b. there is no multiplicative inverse for 6 (mod 9)
    c. 3, since $3 • 3 = 9 = 1$ (mod 4)

22. answers will vary; one possibility is: If $a = 5$, $b = 2$, $c = 3$ and $k = 9$, then $ac = bc$ (mod k) since $15 = 6$ (mod 9). But $a \neq b$ (mod k) in this case since $5 \neq 2$ (mod 9).

23. p^{13} has 14 factors: p^0, p^1, p^2, p^3, . . . , p^{13}

24. a. $2352 = 49 \cdot 48$
    b. $65025 = 15^2 \cdot 17^2$
    c. $15525 = 23 \cdot 25 \cdot 27$

25. No, one integer would have to be even and therefore not prime.

26. 6 is a perfect number

27. a. perfect   b. not perfect   c. not perfect   d. perfect

28. The number is 30. It has the factors 1, 2, 3, 5, $2 \cdot 3$, $2 \cdot 5$, $3 \cdot 5$, and $2 \cdot 3 \cdot 5$.

29. A number in the form p^4 has exactly 5 divisors. Some examples are 16, 81, 625.

30. 12; p^2q (where p and q are prime) has six factors, which are 1, p, p^2, q, pq, and p^2q. Choose the two smallest primes (2 and 3) and this will yield the smallest number of the form p^2q.

31. a. 0, 2, 4, 6, and 8
    b. 3, and 9
    c. 5

32. The answer is 301. Find the LCM of 4, 5, and 6. Look at successive multiples of the LCM, adding 1 to each such multiple, until you find one that is perfectly divisible by 7. Thus, look at numbers of the type $60x + 1$, $x = 1, 2, 3$, etc., until you find one that is divisible by 7.

33. GCD $(x^2, y^2) = 1$. Since x and y do not have any common factors other than 1, the products $x \cdot x$ and $y \cdot y$ will still not have any other common factors.

34. The GCD (a, b) is a factor of both a and b and therefore will be a factor of all multiples of a and b including the LCM (a, b).

35. If a number is divisible by 3 and 4, it is divisible by 12.

36. a. 8   b. 7   c. 2

37. a. false   b. true

38. 15 cookies; least common multiple

39. 1, 2, 3, 4, 6, 8, 9, 12, 16, 18, 24, 36, 48, 72, and 144 rows

40. Suppose the first number is x. Then the other days of the week are $x + 1$, $x + 2$, $x + 3$, $x + 4$, $x + 5$, and $x + 6$. The sum of these numbers is $7x + 21$. If we follow Rebekah's method, we take the first number, x, add 3, and multiply by 7. This gives $(x + 3) \cdot 7 = 7x + 21$. Thus, the two are the same.

41. 600 days; least common multiple

42. Here are some possible solutions. There are more.
    $(12 + 34) + (5 \times 6) + 7 + 8 + 9 = 100$
    $123 - 4 - 5 - 6 - 7 + 8 - 9 = 100$

43. N is greater than 1 because it is 1 more than the product of some whole numbers so it must be positive also. None of 2, 3, 5, . . ., p can divide N because it is one more than a multiple of each of these (since 1 was added to the product).

44. The student found the prime factorization of 58 which is 2 • 29. Since the prime factorization is of the form p • q, where p and q are prime, 58 will have exactly 4 factors.

45. Since zero cannot be multiplied by any number to get a certain number n, zero is not a factor of any number. This is why division by zero is undefined.

46. The proof in #43 would support this thinking.

47. answers will vary

48. a. 900   b. 8100   c. yes, both are factors of 80
    d. increase of 175

49. 51 eggs

50. Yes; here are the solutions:
    2 9-cent, 8 13-cent, 126 3-cent stamps
    5 9-cent, 20 13-cent, 65 3-cent stamps
    8 9-cent, 32 13-cent, 4 3-cent stamps

51. container 4

52. any integers between 20 and 192 except those with 3 or 8 in the units place

53. a. If every digit in the number appears exactly thrice, then the sum of the digits of the number will be a multiple of 3, and hence will be divisible by 3.
    b. We can make a similar conjecture for the number 9.

54. Every palindrome that has an even number of digits is divisible by 11. In every such palindrome, the sum of the alternating digits will always be the same, and so the difference of the two sums will always be 0. Thus, the number will be divisible by 11.

55. Writing a three digit number and then repeating it to get a six digit number is the same as multiplying the three digit number by 1001. Also, 7 • 11 • 13 = 1001. Hence when we divide successively by 7, 11, and 13, we actually divide the number by 1001, thus getting the original number.

56. a. 0; Use the divisibility rule for 5 and since the number has a 5 in the units place, it is divisible by 5
    b. 1; Use the divisibility rule for 3 and add the digits to get 19, and thus a remainder of 1
    c. 1; Look at the pattern of powers of 11 divided by 3. The pattern of remainders is mod 2. Since $4 = 0 \pmod 2$, 11^4 will have the same remainder as 11^0.
    d. 1; Look at the pattern of powers of 5 divided by 3. The pattern of remainders is mod 2. Since $32 = 0 \pmod 2$, 5^{32} will have the same remainder as 5^0.
    e. 4; Look at the pattern of powers of 2 divided by 5. The pattern of remainders is mod 4. Since $102 = 2 \pmod 4$, 2^{102} will have the same remainder as 2^2.

57. 23; Look at the multiples of 7 increased by 2, until you find the required number.

58. The smallest solution to this problem is 25 coins, but the expression 81n + 25, where n = 0, 1, 2 ..., gives all possible values for the number of coins in the chest originally. One method to solve the problem is to let n be the number of coins each pirate got at the final sharing of the coins. We can then work backwards to generate the number of coins at each stage. These will be 3n (just before final sharing), 3/2(3n) + 1, 3/2((9/2)n + 1) + 1, and 3/2((27/4)n + 5/2) + 1. Thus the original number of coins was (81/8)n + 19/4, and we look for a value of n that would make this a counting number.

59. a. The arrangement was (1 + 100) + (2 + 99) + (3 + 98) + ... + (50 + 51). The sum of every pair of numbers within the paranthesis is 101, and there are 50 such pairs (one-half of 100). Thus, the sum of the numbers is 50 • 101 = 5050.

    b. We may try the above process with different sets of numbers. This will help to generalize the method. Thus, the general formula will be (n/2)(n+1).

60. This problem boils down to proving that the numbers are all divisible by 120, which is 2 • 3 • 4 • 5. Notice that for any 5 consecutive numbers, at least 1 of them is divisible by 2, at least 1 is divisible by 3, at least one is divisible by 4, and at least 1 of them is divisible by 5. Hence, the product is divisible by 2 • 3 • 4 • 5 = 120.

61. a. some numbers that have a large number of factors are 24 (8 factors), 30 (8 factors), 36 (9 factors), 40 (8 factors), 48 (10 factors)

    b. some numbers that have only two factors are 29, 31, 37, 41, 43, 47

62.

Number	List of all factors	# of factors	"prime" or prime factorization
26	1, 2, 13, 26	4	2•13
27	1, 3, 9, 27	4	3•3•3
28	1, 2, 4, 7, 14, 28	6	2•2•7
29	1, 29	2	prime
30	1, 2, 3, 5, 6, 10, 15, 30	8	2•3•5
31	1, 31	2	prime
32	1, 2, 4, 8, 16, 32	6	2•2•2•2•2
33	1, 3, 11, 33	4	3•11
34	1, 2, 17, 34	4	2•17
35	1, 5, 7, 35	4	5•7
36	1, 2, 3, 4, 6, 9, 12, 18, 36	9	2•2•3•3
37	1, 37	2	prime
38	1, 2, 19, 38	4	2•19
39	1, 3, 13, 39	4	3•13
40	1, 2, 4, 5, 8, 10, 20, 40	8	2•2•2•5
41	1, 41	2	prime
42	1, 2, 3, 6, 7, 14, 21, 42	8	2•3•7
43	1, 43	2	prime
44	1, 2, 4, 11, 22, 44	6	2•2•11
45	1, 3, 5, 9, 15, 45	6	3•3•5
46	1, 2, 23, 46	4	2•23

47	1, 47	2	prime
48	1, 2, 3, 4, 6, 8, 12, 16, 24, 48	10	2•2•2•2•3
49	1, 49	2	prime
50	1, 2, 5, 10, 25, 50	6	2•5•5

63. a. False; 16 is divisible by 4 but it is not divisible by 12.
    b. True; since 4 is a factor of 12, any number that is divisible by 12 is also divisible by 4.

64. a. Diana must test the largest integer less than or equal to the square root of n since after that any factors will have already been discovered because they will be paired with a number less than the square root of n.
    b. the largest prime whose square is less than p

65. Mod 7 and base 7 are alike in that both use 7 digits; in base 7 the digits are 0-6, and in mod 7 the digits are any seven consecutive digits but usually we use 0-6 or 1-7 (for clock arithmetic). They are also alike in that in both cases grouping is done by sevens (although the grouping is different) and when a group of seven is obtained the situation (counting, performing an operation) changes. In mod 7, this change takes the form of starting over at 0 (or the first digit). In base 7, this change takes the form of regrouping groups of seven. Mod 7 and base 7 are different in that mod 7 is a mathematical system with properties of a mathematical system. Base 7 is a numeration system with properties of a numeration system.

66.

+	0	1	2	3	4	5
0	0	1	2	3	4	5
1	1	2	3	4	5	0
2	2	3	4	5	0	1
3	3	4	5	0	1	2
4	4	5	0	1	2	3
5	5	0	1	2	3	4

x	0	1	2	3	4	5
0	0	0	0	0	0	0
1	0	1	2	3	4	5
2	0	2	4	0	2	4
3	0	3	0	3	0	3
4	0	4	2	0	4	2
5	0	5	4	3	2	1

67. answers will vary; some possibilities are: 4 - 5 = 5, 2 - 5 = 3; 0 - 3 = 3; 3 + 5 = 3; 2 + 4 = 2; 1 + 5 = 5

68. All 4 properties are valid for both addition and multiplication for mod 6 and mod n

69. the nth term of a triangular number is equal to the nth term of a square minus the (n-1)st term of a triangular number; in other words

$$n(n+1)/2 \ = \ n^2 - n(n-1)/2$$

70. From a problem in Chapter 4 we know that $1 + 3 + 5 + \ldots + (2n - 3) + (2n - 1) = n^2$
So, $1 + 3 + 5 + \ldots + (2n - 3) = n^2 - (2n - 1) = (n - 1)^2$
Thus, $1 + 3 + 5 + \ldots + (2n - 3) + (2n - 1) + (2n - 3) + \ldots + 5 + 3 + 1 = (n - 1)^2 + n^2$

71. The pattern of squares is $1^2, 2^2, 3^2, \ldots$. At the nth stage, the number of squares will be n^2. There may be other patterns.

72. The pattern is $0^2 + 1^2, 1^2 + 2^2, 2^2 + 3^2, \ldots$. At the nth stage, the number of squares will be $(n-1)^2 + n^2$. There may be other patterns.

73. 33,552

74. 10 row: 1 9 36 84 126 126 84 36 9 1; next three diagonal sums are 21, 34, 55

75. c. the sum of the numbers in the circle is twice the number two rows directly below the number surrounded by the circled numbers

76. 1, 1, 2, 3, 5, 8, 13, 21, 34, 55, 89, 144, 233, 377, 610, 987
    a. The 4th term is 3, which is odd.
    b. The 6th term is 8, which is even. The 8th term is 21, which is odd. The pattern is odd, odd, even, odd, odd, even, odd, odd, even, . . . In general, the only even terms are those that are multiples of 3 (viz., the 3rd, 6th, 9th, 12th, 15th, . . . terms are even).
    c. The 20th term is odd, the 41st term is odd, and the 250th term is odd.
    d. If the number of the term is divisible by 3 (or is a multiple of 3), then the term is even.

77. Let x be the first number a Fibonacci sequence. Then the first 10 consecutive Fibonacci numbers are: x, x, 2x, 3x, 5x, 8x, 13x, 21x, 34x, 55x. The sum of these 10 numbers is 143x which is divisible by 11, so the sum of any ten consecutive Fibonacci numbers is a multiple of 11.

Chapter 5
1. a. $6 \cdot 6 \cdot 6 = 216$ elements
    b. The set of vowels considered is {a, e, i, o, u}. There are $26 \cdot 5 \cdot 26 = 3,380$ "words." If the letter "y" is considered as a vowel, which it sometimes is, there are $26 \cdot 6 \cdot 26 = 4056$ "words." Note that this solution allows for vowels in the first and third positions of each "word." If vowels are not allowed in these position, there are either $21 \cdot 5 \cdot 21 = 2,205$ or $21 \cdot 6 \cdot 21 = 2,646$ "words."
    c. $52 \cdot 51 = 2,652$ possible sets of 2 cards.
    d. $2 \cdot 2 \cdot 2 \cdot 2 \cdot 2 = 32$ possibilities

2. $2 \cdot 5 = 10$ classifications are needed.

3. For five sandwiches and four drinks, there are $4 \cdot 5 = 20$ sandwich-drink combinations we can choose. If there are an additional three desserts. Then, there are $4 \cdot 5 \cdot 3 = 60$ combinations of sandwich-drink-desserts from which to choose.

4.   The sample space for the 2 experiments is as follows:

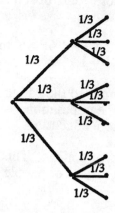

5.   The sample space for the experiment is as follows:

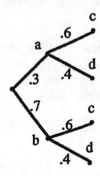

   a. P(a & d) = .3 • .4 = 0.12,
   b. P(a or d) = P(a & c) + P(a & d) + P(b & d) = .3 • .6 + ..3 • .4 + .7 • .4 = .58

6.   a. Sample Space = {0, 1, 2, 3, 4, 5, 6, 7, 8, 9}
     b. The desired event is the set {0, 1, 2, 3, 4}. Hence, P(digit < 5) = 5/10 = 1/2
     c. The desired event is the set {1, 3, 5, 7, 9}. Hence, P(digit is odd) = 5/10 = 1/2
     d. Desired event is {0, 1, 3, 4, 5, 6,7, 8, 9}. Hence, P(digit is not 2) = 9/10.

7.   There is a total of $(2)^4 = 16$ possible outcomes. The subset of the sample space that is favorable to an outcome of *at least* 3 heads is E, where E= {HHHT, HHTH, HTHH, THHH, HHHH}. Hence, P(at least 3 heads) = 5/16.

8.   Two important observations must be made. First, observe that the clock is divided into 60 intervals (minutes). Second, the meaning of "between 5 and 6" must be determined. Notice that there are 5 intervals from 5 to 6. Hence, the desired probability 5/60 = 1/12.

9.   a. $9,000 (about 75% of $12, 000)
     b. $15,000. The value is $5,000 (about 25% of $20,000), so the car has depreciated by $15,000.
     c. $7,000 (about 35% of $20,000)
     d. Dani should do it *within 2 years!* (By the time the car is 2 years old, it has depreciated by more than 50%.

10. According to the table, 38.7% had completed high school, 17.1% had completed 2 years of school beyond high school, and 19.9% had completed 4 or more years of school beyond high school. So, summing these 3 percents, gives 75.7%.

11. According to the table, we must sum 5.5%, 10.0%, 12.8%, and 19.4%. So, the answer is 47.7%

12. In 1987, 24.4% (2.4% + 4.5% + 5.8% + 11.7%) had not completed their high school education. So, assuming that the sample is representative of the population, we should expect 3,000 • 24.4% = 732 people had not completed their high school education.

13. In 1970, 21.3% of the population had taken one or more years of college. This percent is the sum of 10.6% and 10.7%. 10.7/21.3 = 50.2%, which is the percent of people who had begun college and who had finished a 4-year degree.

14. In 1987, 19.9/(17.1 + 19.9) = 53.8%.

15. Post secondary education has steadily increased since 1970 and the percent of people who have not completed high school has steadily decreased.

16. The answer can only be determined by realizing that order matters (that is, vanilla on top and chocolate on bottom is different from chocolate on top and vanilla on the bottom). This means that we want to find how many permutations of the 31 flavors there are when 2 flavors are chosen at a time. So, we get 31 • 30 = 630 double scoops are possible.

17. In this problem, unlike the situation in #16, order does not matter. So, we get (31 • 30)/2 = 315 possible double scoops are possible.

18. Ten people can arrange themselves in 10 • 9 • 8 • 7 • 6 • 5 • 4 • 3 • 2 • 1 = 3,628,800 ways.

19. In bowling, the bowler can knock down 0 - 10 pins on the first roll. The table below summarizes the possibilities:

No. of Pins Knocked Down	No. of Ways
0	1
1	10
2	45
3	120
4	210
5	252
6	210
7	120
8	45
9	10
10	1
Total	1024

20. answers will vary; Here is one example: A coin is flipped and a card is drawn from a standard deck. What is the probability of getting a head and a Jack of hearts?

P(head and Jack of hearts) = P(head) • P(Jack of hearts) = 1/2 • 1/52 = 1/104.

21. answers will vary; Here is one example: Two cards are drawn from a standard deck and the first card is not replaced before drawing the second card. Find the probability of drawing two red cards.

P(red and red) = 26/52 • 25/51 = 650/2652 = (about) 24.5%

22. answers will vary

23.

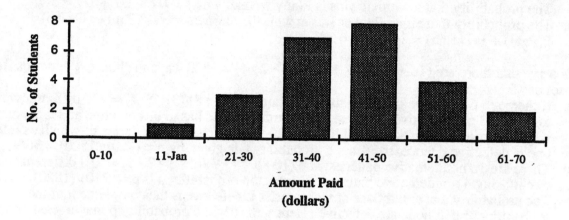

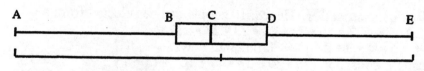

A: minimum amount ($16)   B: 1st quartile ($36)

C: median amount ($42)   D: 3rd quartile amount ($51)

E: maximum amount ($62)

    d. The value of the 3rd quartile is not a whole number because it falls between 50 and 51. Notice that if 50 is chosen as the 3rd quartile amount, only 17 values are below it, which is 68% and if 51 is chosen as the 3rd quartile amount, 19 values fall below it, which is 76%. So the true 3rd quartile value must be between these two amounts.

24. A triangle is formed if and only if the breaks occur on opposite sides of the midpoint of the piece of spaghetti and the breaks are less than 1/2 the length of the piece apart.

P(breaks occur on opposite sides of the midpoint) = 1/2
P(breaks are less than 1/2 of the length of the piece of spaghetti apart) = 1/2
1/2 • 1/2 = 1/4

25. a. The factors of 35 are, 1, 5, 7, and 35. But only 1, 5, and 7 are in the spinner. Hence, P(factor of 35) = 3/8.
    b. P(multiple of 3) = 2/8 = 1/4 since there are only two multiple of 3 on the spinner, namely 3 and 6.
    c. P(even number) = 4/8 = 1/2.
    d. P(6 or 2) = 2/8 = 1/4.
    e. P(11) = 0. *This event is not possible!*

f. A composite number is a number, not equal to 0 or 1, that is *not prime*. A *prime* number is a number other than one whose only factor are 1 and itself. The desired event consists of the elements of the set {4, 6, 8}. Hence, P(composite number) = 3/8.

g. P(neither a prime nor a composite) = P(1) = 1/8.

26. Suppose p denotes the probability that a woman wins. Then P(Fran) = P(Kathy) = P(Dasha) = p, and P(Paul) = P(Norm) = $2p$, since each man is twice as likely to win as any woman. Now the sum of these probability must be 1. That is, $p+p+p+2p+2p=1$. So, $p = 1/7$.

a. The probability that a woman wins is P(any woman wins) = 1/7 + 1/7 + 1/7 = 3/7.

b. The probability that either Paul or Dasha wins the tournament is P(Paul or Dasha)= P(Paul) + P(Dasha) = 2/7 + 1/7 = 3/7.

27. Observe that there are (16 • 15 • 14 • 13)/(4 • 3 • 2 • 1) = 1820 ways to choose 4 batteries from a set of 16.

a. If there are 6 defective batteries, then there are (10 • 9 • 8)/(3 • 2 • 1) = 120 different ways to choose 3 nondefective batteries. The fourth batteries has to be defective and there are 6 ways to choose it. So there are 120 • 6 =720 ways to choose 4 batteries of which exactly one is defective. Hence, the desired probability p is given by p = (720)/(1820) = 36/91.

b. There are 10 nondefective batteries; and (10 • 9 • 8 • 7)/(4 • 3 • 2 • 1) = 210 different ways of choosing 4 nondefective batteries. Hence, the probability p is p = (210)/(1820) = 3/26.

c. The probability that at least one of the batteries is defective is the complement of the probability of that none are defective. Hence, the desired probability p that at least one of the batteries is defective is p= 1 - (3/26) = 23/26.

28. a. There are 30 individuals altogether. Hence, 10 people can be selected from a group of 30 people in (30 • 29 • 28 • 27 • 26 • 25 • 24 • 23 • 22 • 21) ÷ (10 • 9 • 8 • 7 • 6 • 5 • 4 • 3 • 2 • 1) = 30,045,015 ways.

b. The 5 smokers can be chosen in (20 • 19 • 18 • 17 • 16) ÷ (5 • 4 • 3 • 2 • 1) = 15,504 ways. The nonsmokers can be selected in (10 • 9 • 8 • 7 • 6) ÷ (5 • 4 • 3 • 2 • 1) = 252 ways. Hence, there 15,504 • 252 = 3,907,008 ways in which this can be done!

29. a. Sample Space = {1, 2, 3, 4, 5, 6}; Probability distribution: P(1) = P(2) = P(3) = P(4) = P(5) = P(6) = 1/6.

b. Sample Space = {1, 2, 3, 4, 5, 6, 8, 10, 12, 9, 15, 18, 16, 20, 24, 25, 30, 36}; Probability distribution: P(1) = P(36) = P(9) = P(16) = P(25) = P(36) = 1/36; P(2) = P(3) = P(5) = P(8) = P(10) = P(15) = P(18) = P(20) = P(24) = P(30) = 2/36 = 1/18; P(4) = 3/36 = 1/12; P(6) = 4/36 = 1/9.

30. The number of ways 5 transistors can be chosen from a set of 200 transistors is (200 • 199 • 198 • 197 • 196)/(5 • 4 • 3 • 2 • 1) = 2,535,650,040. To solve the problem we can take a short cut by using the principle of "probability complement." That is, we can obtain the probability that the box is rejected by: P(box is rejected) = 1 - P(box is not rejected) = 1 - P(none are defective). Note that in order for none of the transistors to be defective they all would have to be chosen from the items that are not defective; there are 190 of such transistors. So, P(none are defective) = (190 • 189 • 188 • 187 • 186)/(5 • 4 • 3 • 2 • 1) ÷ (200 • 199 • 198 • 197 • 196)/(5 • 4 • 3 • 2 • 1) = (1,956,800,538) ÷ (2,535,650,040) = .77. Hence, P(box is rejected) = 1 - 0.77 = 0.23.

31. a.

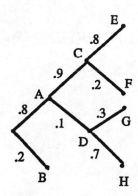

A: Sets alarm

B: Does not set alarm

C: Alarm rings

D: Alarm does not ring

E: Wakes in time

F: Does not wake in time

G: Wakes in time

H: Does not wake in time

b. From the above tree, the probability that Jamal wakes in time for his 8:30 class is
P(in time for class) = $0.8 \cdot 0.9 \cdot 0.8 + 0.8 \cdot 0.1 \cdot 0.3 = 0.6$

32.

a.

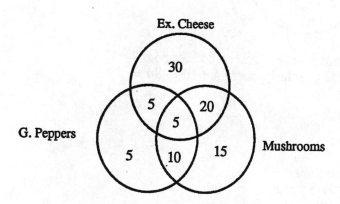

b. 15 people wanted only mushrooms

c. 10 people wanted green peppers & mushrooms, but no extra cheese

33.

a.

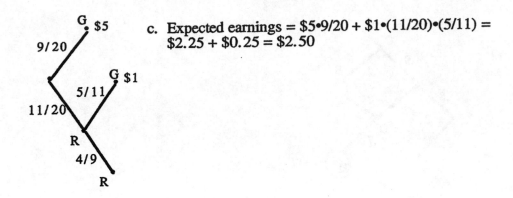

c. Expected earnings = $5•9/20 + $1•(11/20)•(5/11) =
$2.25 + $0.25 = $2.50

34.

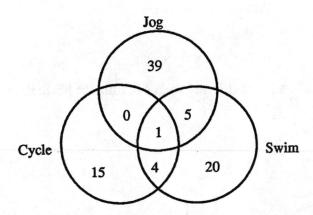

Summing all values in the diagram givers a total of 84. Since
there are 100 faculty who exercise regularly, there are 100 - 84 =
16 who do none of these three.

39 only jog.

35. a. There are $(2)^8 = 256$ possible outcomes.
b. There are 16 ways to have exactly 3 heads
c. 247 outcomes have at least 2 heads.
d. 203 outcomes have 4 or 5 heads.
e. The entire sample space could be listed in a systematic manner and then inspected to see
how many of them contain 2 or more heads. Another, more efficient way to determine
how many outcomes have at least 2 heads is to determine how many outcomes have fewer
than 2 heads and then subtract the result from 256.

36. a. The sample space is S={ M, I, S, S, I, S, S, I, P, P, I}.
Note that the sample space is not {M, I, S, P}.
b. The event, "the letter chosen is a vowel" is the subset, {I}.

37. a. 9/60 = 3/20
b. 12/60 or 1/5

38. P(3 or more correct out of 5 questions) = 16/32 = 1/2

39. a. Both players have the same chance of winning because both can win in 2 ways of the 4 possible outcomes.
    b. Yes, the game is fair because the two players have the same likelihood of winning.

40. 13/52 = 1/4 probability of drawing a heart.
    a. 1/4 • 1/4 = 1/16
    b. 1/4 • 12/51 = 1/17

41. Let b= boy and g= girl.
    The sample space S is: S = {bbb, bgg, bgb, bbg, gbb, ggb, gbg, ggg}
    Favorable outcomes are bgg, bgb, bbg, gbb, ggb, gbg, ggg.
    Hence, the probability is 7/8.

    Alternatively, observe that P(at least one girl) = 1 - P(all 3 children are boys)
    But P(all 3 children are boys) = 1/8. Hence, P(at least one girl) = 1 - 1/8 = 7/8.

    You must assume that the probability of a boy being born is equal to the probability of a girl being born.

42. The problem assumes that a slice means "a cut from one side of the pizza to the other" (if it has a rectangular shape). It also assumes that slices are straight line segments (not, for example, a curve or spiral cut of some sort). With these assumptions in mind, it is possible to get a maximum of 56 pieces.

43. 45 matches

44. 9 matches

45. 45 handshakes

46. answers will vary depending on the scenario devised to pair the car speeds with other data

47. answers will vary

48.

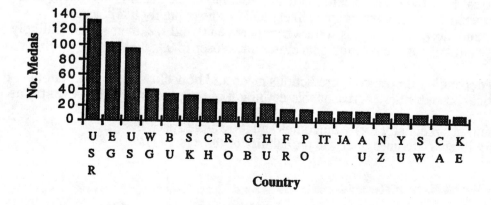

49. Various interpretations are possible. For example, one could compare Communist bloc (those that existed in 1988) countries with other countries and conclude that they won far more medals that non-Communist countries. The countries could be grouped by continent (viz., Africa, Asia, Australia, Europe, North America, South America) and draw conclusions about medal distribution (e.g., no South American countries were among the top 20 medal winners.)

50.

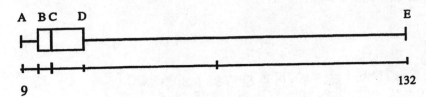

A: minimum number of medals (9)
B: 1st quartile (14)
C: median (19.5)
D: 3rd quartile (35)
E: maximum number of medals (132)

51. The number of medals won by the USSR, East Germany, and the USA are outliers using the definition given.

52. median: 16; 1st quartile: 13; 3rd quartile: 24

53. The median probably best represents the average number of medals won by the top 20 countries—19 or 20. It would be a misrepresentation to eliminate the outliers by using the median of the other 17 countries. An even better indicator of the average number of medals won is probably the interquartile range because 55% of the values fall within this range.

54. The key to these questions is to be aware of what it means for an event to be certain, impossible, highly likely, and highly unlikely. The degree of uncertainty can be quantified through the notion of the relative frequency of a specific outcome:

<u>number of times the outcome occurs</u>
total number of trials

If this fraction is equal to 1, the event is certain. If it is equal to 0, the event is impossible. If it is somewhere between 1 and 1/2, the event is likely and becomes highly likely as the fraction gets closer and closer to 1. If it is somewhere between 0 and 1/2, the event is unlikely and becomes highly unlikely as the fraction gets closer and closer to 0.

55. Answers will vary depending on personal predictions made and how close these predictions were to the theoretical probabilities. A reasonable definition of the probability of an event is as follows:

If an event has n equally likely outcomes and its sample space has m equally likely outcomes, then the probability of the event is n/m.

56. A method for determining the probability of an event is the following:

List the sample space for the experiment and note how many outcomes are in it. Then to determine the probability of an event in that sample space, find how many outcomes are in that event and divide that number by the number of outcomes in the sample space. (This method works well only if the sample space is relatively small.)

57. An <u>outcome</u> of an experiment is the result of performing the experiment. The sample space of an experiment is the set of all possible outcomes of the experiment. An <u>event</u> in an experiment is a subset of the sample space of the experiment. The event is said to have occurred if the outcome of an experiment corresponds to one of the elements of the event.

58. a. It is possible, but highly unlikely if the coin is fair.
  b. P(15 consecutive heads) = $(1/2)^{15}$, which is approximately .00003. This probability is determined with the assumptions that each head has probability 1/2 of occurring and each toss of the coin is independent of each other toss.
  c. On the 16th toss, the probability is 1/2 that the outcome will once again be a head because the tosses are independent.

59. P(E) is always less than or equal to 1 because the number of outcomes in an event must be less than or equal to the number of outcomes in the sample space. P(E) is always greater than or equal to 0 because P(E) = n/m and $m > 0, n >= 0$.

60. The number of ways that a collection of r elements can be selected from a set of n distinct elements is given by

$$\frac{n \times (n-1) \times (n-2) \times \ldots \times [(n-r)+1]}{r \times (r-1) \times \ldots \times 2 \times 1}$$

61. Many graphs and charts are possible; one is given below:

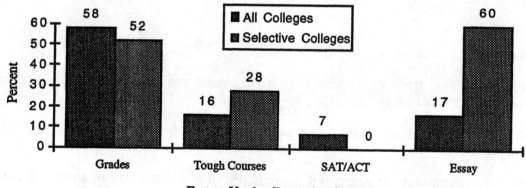

Factors Used to Determine Admission

Chapter 6
1. team

2. blend

3. math is fun

4. Indiana

5.   answers will vary

6.   a. 9 out of 12 should be shaded   b. 4 out of ten sections should be shaded
     c. 5/7 should be placed a little over halfway between 0 and 1

7.   a. 1/16; 1/4 • 1/4 = 1/16   1/12; 1/2 • 1/6 = 1/12
         1/4; 1/2 • 1/2 = 1/4   1/8; 1/2 • 1/4 = 1/8
     b. answers will vary

8.   answers will vary

9.   answers will vary; some possibilities are:
     a. 1/3, 2/6   b. -6/10, -9/15   c. 0/1, 0/5

10. answers will vary; diagram should illustrate that for congruent regions, 2 out of 3 sections is
     equivalent to 6 out of 9 sections

11. a.78/77   b. 17/91   c. -17/45

12. a. diagram should have 3 out of 5 equivalent sections shaded, and then 1/3 of the shaded
         region cross shaded
     b. diagram should have 1 out of 2 equivalent sections shaded, and then 2/9 of the shaded
         region cross shaded

13. a. 35/78   b. -32/63   c. 34/63

14. a. 7/14, 7/11, 7/9   b. -7/8, -3/5, -8/19

15. answers may vary
     a. 1518, 31/36   b. -17/28, -35/56   c. 144/209, 145/209

16. a. 1/3   b. 14   c. 7/2

17. place appropriately in this order: .75 (b), 1.125 (c), 2 (d), 2.25 (a)

18. answers will vary; One possibility is: Moses ate 1/3 of a pizza and Rebekah ate 1/4 of a pizza.
     How much more pizza did Moses eat? 1/3 - 1/4 = 4/12 - 3/12 = 1/12 of a pizza

19. Divide the paper into tenths and shade two tenths. Show by folding, for example, that this is
     one-third of six tenths.

20. The model should show that one group of .6 is contained in .9 and one-half of another group
     of .6 is contained in the remaining. So .6 is contained in .9 one and one-half times.

21. it would need to have a denominator with less than or equal value than the other

22. 3/8

23. illustrations will vary; 9/10

24. The illustration should show that one group of 4/9 is contained in 6/9, and the remaining
     represents 1/2 of 4/9. So 4/9 is contained in 6/9 one and one-half times.

25. 14

26. no, taking one-third would be the same as dividing the number by 3

27. charge $3.33 for 576 square inches of material

28. 4 times faster

29. 18 2/21 pizzas

30. 5 5/14 days

31. when n is a multiple of two

32. e

33. 15 bookmarks; 3/4 inch left over

34. a. 11/22, 11/16, 11/13
    b. 23/16, 33/16, 3
    c. -17/30, -19/36, -1/5
    d. 3/4, 5/6, 7/8
    e. -1/6, -1/78, -1/8
    f. 3/10, 2/5 = 4/10
    g. 0/7 = 0/17, 3/17
    h. -2/3, -4/7, 3/4, 4/5

35. a. a < c   b. b > d   c. answers will vary; a/b = c/d

36. 5/6

37. 5/6 = 1/2 + 1/3   13/12 = 1/3 + 3/4   13/36 = 1/4 + 1/9   26/21 = 2/3 + 4/7

38. a. <   b. CT   c. CT   d. >
    e. CT   f. CT   g. =   h. <

39. There are infinitely many answers. Some possibilities are:
    a. 1/3, 4/5, 15/2   b. 2/3, 3/10, 1/10   c. 3/4, 1/2, 4/3

40. a. sometimes; it's not true if x < 0 and y > 0
    b. sometimes; it's not true if x ≤ 1
    c. sometimes; it's true if m = p

41. 2/3 ÷ 2/5 is asking "how many 2/5 are in 2/3?"; since there are 5/2 2/3s in 1 unit, then we must multiply 2/3 by 5/2 in order to find out how many 2/5 are in 2/3; illustration should demonstrate why there are 5/2 2/5s in one unit

42. When making single-color trains, rods that have only two single-color trains are prime because they have only the rod itself and a group of 1 cm rods (white) as trains. This corresponds to a prime number having only two factors, 1 and the prime number. Rods that have more than two single-color trains are composite because they have other factors that are represented by the rods of different lengths.

Chapter 7
1. answers may vary; a block with 2 out of the 10 units shaded (or 20 out of 100 units, etc.)

2. a. 5.253   b. -.78   c. -5.21

3. a. 12.084   b. 1.625   c. 6

4. answers may vary; some possibilities are 29/144, 1/5

5. a. $3.2, 3.\overline{22}, 3.23, 3.\overline{23}, 3.2\overline{3}$ b. $-1.4\overline{54}, -1.\overline{454}, -1.45\overline{4}, -1.454, -1.45$

6. a. $.02\overline{5}, .\overline{02}, .02, .0\overline{02}, .002$ b. $-1.19, -1.\overline{19}. -1.192, -1.2\overline{1}, -1.\overline{21}$

7. write the decimals out to several more places and then compare

8. answers will vary; some possibilities are .841, .8433

9. answers will vary; some possibilities are -2.295, -2.297

10. a. 3.29, 3.2957, 3.230525, 3.23057, 3.231   b. $-.73\overline{7}, -7373, -.737, .7\overline{3}$

11. e

12. a. a flat   b. the result is: 1 cube, 8 flats, 1 long

13. a. .625   b. $.\overline{3}$ c. $.91\overline{6}$

14. a. -5 8/25   b. 4 11/500   c. 25 3/20

15. a. 13/30   b. 35/99

16. a, c

17. answers will vary; some possibilities are $\sqrt{(7/10)}, \sqrt{(.9)}$

18. yes, it is equivalent to 2/3

19.

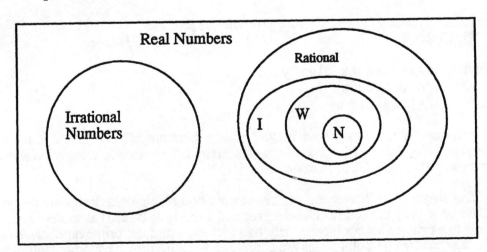

I = set of Integers, W = set of Whole numbers, N = set of Natural numbers

20. answers will vary; some possibilities are: 13, 4; 1, 5; 50, 6

21. 3/5

22. answers will vary

23. the ratio of boys to girls will become smaller

24. if it cannot be written as a terminating or repeating decimal

25. you must consider that values exist continuously to the right of the repeated value

26. set the value equal to x; multiply both sides of this equation by a power of 10 until the repeating decimal is isolated on the right of the decimal point; then subtract the first equation from the second equation and solve for x

27. only after performing the multiplication or division is it essential to determine where the decimal place should be located

28. answers will vary; some possibilities are:
    a. (.1 + .2) ÷ .3   b. .8 • .7   c. .4 ÷ .9
    d. .9 ÷ .2   e. .6 • .2   f. .3 + .4 - .7
    g. (.3 • .5) + .1   h. (.1 - .9) ÷ .2

29. a. 88.6; 5 • 17 is 85   b. 15.6; 68 ÷ 4 is 17   c. 14.6; 6 • 17 is 102, 102 • .1 is 10.2
    d. .132; 16 • 8 is a three digit number, then divided by 1000 would be a three-digit decimal
    e. 4.71; .15 goes into .7 around 4 times   f. 4.68; 400 ÷ 80 is 5
    g. 2.2; .09 goes into .198 around 2 times   h. .7615; .9 goes into .7 around .7 times
    i. 2.096641; 5 • .3 is 1.5

30. 31 cents

31. A fraction can be written as a terminating decimal if it can be expressed with a denominator that is a power of 10. But 7, having prime factors other than 2 and/or 5, is not a factor of any power of 10.

32. both are correct

33. 11 1/9%, 22 2/9%, 66 2/3%

34. yes, each side of the square could be $\sqrt{5}$ cm, which is possible to construct by constructing a right triangle with legs of length 1 cm and 2 cm. Then the hypotenuse will be $\sqrt{5}$ cm. Use this length to construct a square with sides of length $\sqrt{5}$ cm and the area will be 5 cm².

35. Yes, each side of the square could be $\sqrt{11}$ cm, which is possible to construct. Construct right triangles with these sides: 1, 1, $\sqrt{2}$ and 1, 2, $\sqrt{5}$. Then using these hypotenuses ($\sqrt{2}$ and $\sqrt{5}$) as legs, construct a new triangle having a hypotenuse of length $\sqrt{7}$. Use this segment (of length $\sqrt{7}$ cm) and a segment of length 2 cm to construct another right triangle; this triangle will have a hypotenuse of length $\sqrt{11}$ cm. Use this length to construct a square with sides of length $\sqrt{11}$ cm and the area will be 11 cm².

36. right triangles can help in analyzing irrational numbers, especially those with square roots, since finding the length of a side using the Pythagorean Theorem involves the use of square roots

37. a. 4%   b. 32%   c. 64%

38. a. ≈ 4.9%, ≈ 34.6%, ≈ 60.5%
    b. 6.25%, 37.5%, 56.25%
    c. ≈8.2%, ≈40.8%, ≈51%
    d. ≈2,8%, ≈27.8∞, ≈69.4%
    e. $(400/n)\%$, $(400(n-2)/n)\%$, $(100(n-2)^2/n)\%$

39. answers will vary; $\sqrt{2}$, .121221222..., $\sqrt{5}$

40. 57th place; 1/17 is a repeating decimal; the entire block repeats: .0588235294117647

Chapter 8

1. .01 billion per year between 1900 and 1910; .04 billion per year between 1900 and 1990

2. 152 people per minute (includes 1980, 1984 and 1988 having 366 days each)

3. answers may vary; One estimation is 6.1 billion people, as this is consistent with the prior two decades' increase of 0.8 billion people. (Another could be 6.2 billion.)

4. Factors might include famine, war, natural disasters, birth control, etc..

6. 1.94 billion people per year for 1900 to 1990; slower than 1980 to 1990

7. 1950 to 1960, and 1960 to 1970

8. 3,942,000 babies born per 365-day year

9. One reasonable answer is 273,000,000 people in 2000, as trends from the past few decades denote increases of just under 25,000,000 per decade.

10. One factor to consider is immigration.

11. Lowest rate of change during 1930-1940 decade. The Great Depression is a likely culprit.

12.

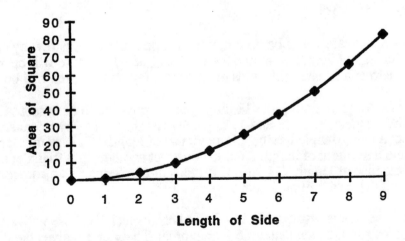

12. (cont'd)

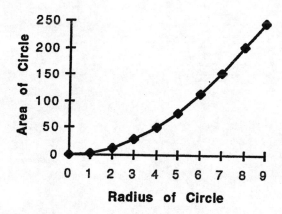

' Both graphs curve upward rather rapidly. The circle graph increases much faster than the square graph. (1 times faster)

13.

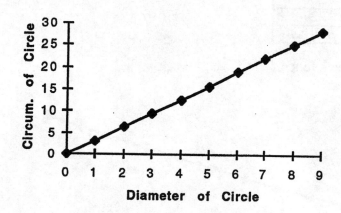

The slope of the line is π (3.14...).

14.

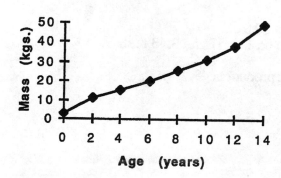

15   a. 2(10) + 2(40) = 100 ft

b.

Side Length	Total Fence Needed
3.4	242 (X)
3.5	236
5	170
10	100
20	80
30	87
40	100
50	116
60	133
70	151
80	170
90	189
100	208
110	227
120	247(X)

X—denotes too much fence

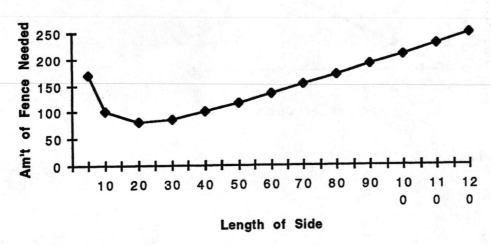

c. The least amount of fencing needed is 80 feet.
d. Yes, it is possible. The sides need to be 116.57 and 3.43 feet.

16. The largest product is 625. The smallest product is 49.

17. (6)(7)(7) = 294. (1)(1)(18) = 18.

18. 2^{50}

19.

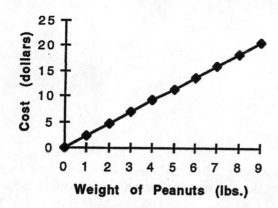

The slope of the line is 2.29. The slope is the rate of change of the cost and the cost increases at the rate of 2.29 per pound.

20. 500,000 copies will be required in order for the cost of the options to be equal. Less, and the $17,500 copier will be cheaper. More, and the $20,000 copier will be. Costs will be equal when $20,000 + .02x = 17,500 + .025x$; $x = 500,000$.

21. 1.8614 feet $< x < 3.1923$ feet

22. Area $= 4x^2 + 100x$

23. $200 < 4x^2 + 100x < 360$

24. Let $C(x)$ represent the size of each member's contribution. The size of the contribution will decrease as the number of people making the trip increases. $C(x) = 180/x$, $x = 0$.

25. The total cost, $C(x)$, increases as the number of pictures developed increases. $C(x) = 2 + .25x$

    The cost per picture, $c(x)$, decreases as the number of pictures developed increases; $c(x) = 2/x + .25$

For each of the following (#s 26-29), the requested response is underlined.

26. Input	Output		27. Input	Output		28. Input	Output		29. Input	Output
1	18		50	53		14	17		2	-20
2	21		60	63.6		-20	0		4	20
3	24		70	74.2		20	20		6	20/3
9	42		400	424		230	125		23	1
x	3x+15		x	1.06x		x	x/2 + 10		x	20/(x-3)
a/3 - 5	a		a/1.06	a		2a - 20	a		(20/a) + 3	a

30.

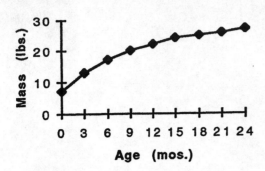

The weight of the average American baby increases in weight over time. According to this data, the amount of increase decreases over time. The variables could be said to be positively related.

31.

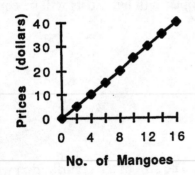

The price of a bag of mangoes steadily increases as the number of mangoes increases. The rate of increase stays constant, as the price per mango is $2.50. The variables are positively and linearly related.

32.

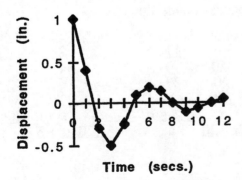

The pattern of the graph fluctuates from decreasing to increasing over time. The size of the fluctuation from zero decreases over time.

33. **a.** The amount of time it takes to mow the lawn with a push mower is a function of the height of the grass at the time of the mowing.

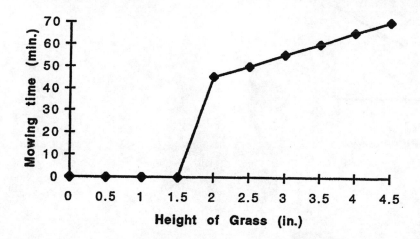

b. The amount of time it takes to hand wash and wipe a certain number of dishes as a function of the number of people "doing the dishes."

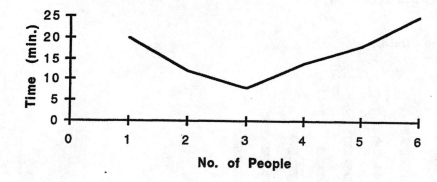

34.

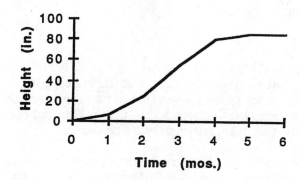

35.

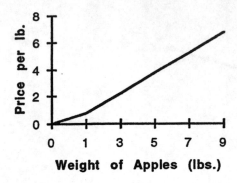

36.

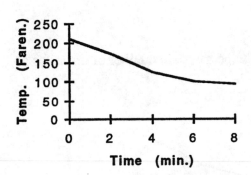

37.

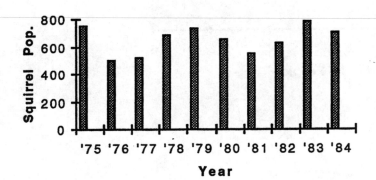

Headline: "Squirrel Population Has Its Ups and Downs"
Opening Paragraph: (Paragraphs will vary, but all should indicate that the population of squirrels seems to have followed a pattern over the past 10 years (the period for which data was collected). The range in population has been from about 500 to nearly 800, but between these two extremes there is a definite rise and fall in approximately a sine curve.

38. a. 1, 2, 4, 7, 11 For any number in the sequence, sum the number and its position in the sequence to get the next number in the sequence. (e.g., 4 is 3rd in the sequence, 4+3=7)
    b. 1, 2, 4, 7, 12 Starting with the 3rd digit, sum the two previous digits and 1 to get the next digit. (e.g., For the 4th digit, the 2nd and 3rd (2 and 4) total 6, plus 1 equals 7)
    c. 1, 2, 4, 7, 13 Starting with the 4th digit, add the previous three to get the next digit. (e.g., For the 4th digit, sum the first three (1+2+4) to get 7)

39. 122° F; 50(9/5) + 32 = 122

40. 77° F to 104° F corresponds to 25° C to 40° C

41. 98.6° F corresponds to 37° C

42. -40° C = -40° F

43. F = (9/5)C + 32; C = (5/9)(F - 32)

44. This approach would work for approximations, but while there is a little over 6% error for freezing (0° C), there is over 11% error for 1000° C. The accuracy required determines the appropriateness of the estimation.

45. This is never true. First, F = (9/5)C + 32. Next, if the statement were true, then 2F = (9/5)2C + 32. With substitution, 2[(9/5)C + 32] = (9/5)2C + 32, which implies that 64 = 32, which is not true.

46. Things to consider are the fact that the carrier makes a dollar per paper, and makes an additional $20 to the number of papers delivered, no matter what the number. The more one is willing to work, if available, the more money one can earn.

47. a.

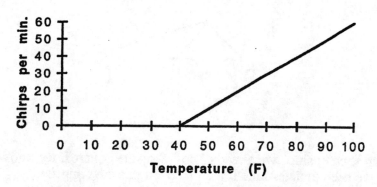

Temperature   (F)

  b. The function is linear, increasing from a temperature of 40 degrees on, is 0 below 40 degrees, and probably has no meaning after the temperature reaches some value above 100 degrees.
  c. Minimum value for "chirps per minute" is 0. Maximum value is likely to be about 60 or 70 chirps per minute.

48. a. $10
     b. P(x) = 10x - 250, where P(x) is the profit earned, and x is # of lawns mowed
     c. 125 lawns
     d. P(x) = 10x - 195
     e. 120 lawns

Chapter 9
1.   a. 6   b. 10

2.   two lines that do not intersect may be parallel or they may be skew

3.   three points always lie in the same plane (are coplanar) but four points may not be coplanar

4.   yes, if the line is in the same plane as the line it is perpendicular to

5.   a. yes   b. yes, as long as the obtuse angle is between the two congruent sides
     c. yes   d. no

6.   a. a, c, d and f are congruent angles; b and e are supplementary angles

7.   50° and 40°, respectively

8.   a. copy the segment AB and copy <Q on both ends of the segment; end the sides of <Q until
         they meet
     b. copy the segment AB, mark off arcs congruent to 2•AB from both endpoints A and B, and
         where the arcs meet is the third vertex; connect segment AB to the third vertex

9.   constructions

10. a. i. rhombus   ii. trapezoid
     b. i. false, it could be a rectangle   ii. true, all the angles must be 90° so it must be a
                                                      rectangle

11. a. 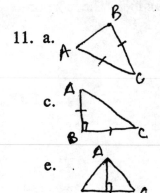   b.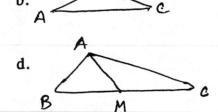

     c.   d.

     e.

12. a. the length of a side in each square; since we already know they are squares, we know their
         angles are congruent and we need to determine if their side lengths are congruent
     b. the length of two adjacent sides in each rectangle; since we already know they are
         rectangles, we know their angles are congruent and we need to determine if their side
         lengths are congruent
     c. the length of two adjacent sides and the measure of the included angle in each
         parallelogram; since we already know they are parallelograms, we know the opposite
         sides are parallel and we need to determine if the opposite sides and opposite angles are
         congruent

13. a. any two rectangles are not always similar since their side lengths could be in different
         ratios
     b. any two circles are always similar since the ratio of the radii is constant
     c. any two regular polygons are always similar if they are the same polygon since their
         angles will always be congruent and the ratio of their side lengths will be the same for all
         corresponding sides

14. a. false   b. true   c. false   d. false   e. true

15. a. true   b. false, they may have different radii lengths
    c. false, their side lengths may be in different ratios   d. true
    e. false, their side lengths may not be congruent   f. true

16. a and d are similar

17. a. the alternate rectangles are similar (i.e., every other rectangle)
    b. the diagonals of similar rectangles will line up when nested in this way

18. a. opposite sides parallel and one right angle
    b. opposite sides parallel and two consecutive sides congruent
    c. opposite sides parallel, one right angle, and two consecutive sides congruent

19. since $\triangle$ BEF is similar to $\triangle$ DEA by AAA, then BE = 3 and ED = 4.5.

20. $s = (n - 2)150$

21. use the formula $(n - 2)180$ or divide the polygon into triangles to find that the sum of the measures of the angles is 900°

22.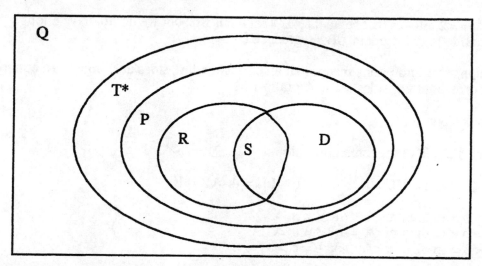

*with trapezoid defined as a quadrilateral with at least one pair of opposite sides parallel

23. a. <1 and <3 are supplementary
    b. <6 and <7 are vertical and therefore congruent
    c. <2 and <11 are congruent (alternate exterior angles)
    d. m<8 = m<4 + m<5 since they are alternate interior angles

24. a. 70°   b. 60°   c. 60°   d. 110°   e. 70°

25. 120°; there are 4 triangles that can be formed in a hexagon so the sum of the measures of the angles is 720°; since the hexagon is regular, all six angles are congruent, thus they must each be 120°

26. 135°; there are 6 triangles that can be formed in an octagon so the sum of the measures of the angles is 1080°; since the octagon is regular, all eight angles are congruent, thus they must each be 135°

27. two parallel lines would form three regions and two intersecting lines would form four regions

28. yes, if the line is lying in the plane

29. they are all a set of points; a ray has one endpoint, a segment has two endpoints, and line does not have endpoints

30. both terms refer to points that lie together; for collinear points, they lie on the same line; for coplanar points, they lie on the same plane

31. yes, if all the lines are in the plane

32. yes

33. this is not a good definition since the definition must include that the angles have a common vertex and no common interior points

34. this is not a good definition since the definition must include that adjacent sides are congruent

35. no; m<1 = m<2 tells us that segment AD ∥ segment BC, but we do not have enough information to tell if segment AB ∥ segment CD

36. no, two congruent polygons means that all corresponding sides and angles are congruent, and thus all corresponding sides are in the ratio 1 : 1.

37. regular polygons

38. the included angle or the remaining side

39. a. 90°   b. CD = 4   c. EC = 4, AF = 10

40. a. If a > b > c, then m<A < m<B < m<C
    b. If a = b < c, then m<A = m<B < m<C
    c. If m<B = m<C > m<A, then b = c > a

41. a. always   b. sometimes   c. always   d. sometimes

42. a. sometimes b. true if an isosceles trapezoid; false if not

43. yes, since with two angles given, the third angles are determined and they must be congruent to each other; thus by AAA the triangles are similar

44. yes, if all three pairs of corresponding sides are proportional, the triangles are similar

45. no, rectangles always have their angles congruent, but the sides could be in different ratios

46. no, rectangles always have their angles congruent, but the sides could be in different ratios

47. yes, since all angles in rectangles are congruent

48. a. 4/6 = 3/4.5 = 2/3 since all are in the ratio of 1 : 1.5
    c. yes

49. a. the sum of the measures of the angles in a triangle is 180°
    c. yes

50. x = 20/3, y cannot be determined; x = 6

51. CDA

52. Form an equilateral triangle from two 30°-60°-90° triangles. All angles will be 60° and all sides congruent. The measure of one leg of a smaller triangle will be one-half the measure of any side of the equilateral triangle and hence the side opposite the 30° angle is half as long as the hypotenuse in one of the original triangles.

53. m<w = 80°, UV = 6, UW = 5, WV = 4, m<Z = 80°, m<X = 60°, m<Y = 40°, VUW

54. a. the base angles of an isosceles triangle are congruent
    b. use the angle bisector of the vertex angle

55. use similar triangles ABC and CBD or that <DCB and <A are both complementary to <ACD

56. Rebekah is correct. If two angles in one triangle are congruent to two angles in another, then the third angles must also be congruent and then the triangles in this case are congruent by ASA.

57. a. connect two midpoints and show that the newly formed triangle is similar to the original triangle by SAS for similarity; then since the ratio of two of the sides is 1 : 2, the thirds must also have this ratio so the third side is equal to 1/2 of the length of the original third side; also all angles must be congruent and so the line segment joining the midpoints must be parallel to the third side because corresponding angles formed by the transversal are congruent
    b. draw the diagonals in the quadrilateral and then connect the midpoints as specified; using the proof in a., pairs of opposite segments are parallel because they are both parallel to the diagonal drawn (the diagonals form triangles that allow us to use the results from a); since both pairs of opposite sides are parallel, the quadrilateral is a parallelogram
    c. draw the diagonals in the rectangle and then connect the midpoints as specified; from b. we have that the quadrilateral formed is a parallelogram; furthermore, since from a. the segments connecting midpoints are half the length of the diagonals, and the diagonals are congruent in a rectangle, all four segments are congruent; thus, the quadrilateral is a rhombus

58. the smaller triangle is similar to the original triangle by the SAS property for similarity

59. a. the two base angles in each triangle are 45°; the hypotenuse in Δ ABC is 4√2 cm and the hypotenuse in Δ DEF is 8√2 cm
    b. the triangles are similar by AA similarity
    c. the triangles are not congruent because their corresponding sides are not congruent
    d. area Δ ABC = 8 square cm, area Δ DEF = 32 square cm

60. her proof is not correct because the way she has drawn her triangles, she is also including the measures of the angles around the interior point. In order to find the sum of the angle measures using this method, she needs to take the total (1800°) and subtract 360° because this is the sum of the angle measures around the interior point.

61. 180°

62. Let the unlabeled angles of the three triangles be labeled x, y, and z. The corresponding vertical angles of each of these angles, together with these angles forms a circle (with 360°). Then $2x + 2y + 2z = 360$ and so $x + y + z = 180$. Thus, $a + b + x + c + d + y + e + f + z = 3$ (180) and so $a + b + c + d + e + f = 360°$

63. *trapezoid*—quadrilateral with at least one pair of opposite sides parallel; *parallelogram*—quadrilateral with both pairs of opposite sides parallel; *rhombus*—parallelogram with one pair of congruent adjacent sides; *rectangle*—parallelogram with one right angle; *square*—parallelogram with one pair of congruent adjacent sides and one right angle; *kite*—quadrilateral with two pairs of congruent adjacent sides; *isosceles trapezoid*—trapezoid with at least one pair of congruent opposite sides

64. in general, the more properties a quadrilateral has, the farther down the tree diagram is it

65. the further down you go on the tree diagram, the more symmetry there is

66. a. There are 10 different triangles with perimeter 12 units if the sides must all be whole numbers: (2,5,5), (5,2,5), (5,5,2), (3,4,5), (3,5,4), (4,3,5), (4,5,3), (5,3,4), (5,4,3), (4,4,4).
    b. There are 216 possible outcomes for rolling 3 dice. Of these possible outcomes, 40 of them can be lengths of sides of a triangle. So, the probability is $40/216 = 5/27$.
    c. Three numbers can be the lengths of a triangle if and only if the sum of any pair of the 3 numbers is greater than the third number (i.e., for any 3 numbers x, y, and z, $x + y > z$, $x + z > y$, and $y + z > x$).

67. a. between 26 and 72 miles apart
    b. You can determine the range by finding the difference (for the minimum distance) and the sum (for the maximum distance)

68. The probability that the 3 pieces could be the sides of a triangle is 1/4 (see "Exercises and More Problems" in Chapter 5). Infinitely many right triangles can be formed if any lengths are possible. However, if the lengths of the 3 sides must be whole numbers, only a 3-4-5 right triangle is possible.

69. a. the new triangle is bigger; the ratio of the sides is 3 : 1
    b. the new triangle is smaller; the ratio of the sides is 1/2 : 1
    c. the new triangle is the same as the original

70. a. 2^3 b. 3^3 c. n^3

71. it will be a rhombus; draw the diagonals in the rectangle and then connect the midpoints as specified; we have that the quadrilateral formed is a parallelogram; furthermore, since the segments connecting midpoints are half the length of the diagonals, and the diagonals are congruent in a rectangle, all four segments are congruent; thus, the quadrilateral is a rhombus; we cannot prove that the angles of EFGH are right angles, so the most we can say is that the figure is a rhombus

72. The proof makes use of the following diagram.

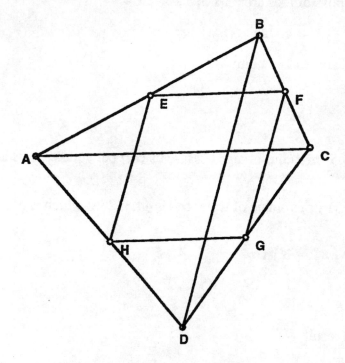

Proof: Notice that FG connects the midpoints of two sides of ΔBCD. So, by a previously established theorem, FG is parallel to BD. And, EH connects the midpoints of two sides of ΔABD, which means that EH is also parallel to BD. So, FG is parallel to EH. Similarly, it can be shown that EF is parallel to HG. Thus, by definition of parallelogram (a quadrilateral whose opposite sides are parallel), EFGH is a parallelogram.

Chapter 10
1. a. 200 square inches   b. 60 inches

2. 20 cm; the width must be 4 cm and so the perimeter = 4 + 6 + 4 + 6

3. 1 yd x 24 yd; 2 yd x 12 yd; 3 yd x 8 yd; 4 yd x 6 yd

4. 8 square feet

5. 8 square feet

6. 10.25 cm

7. 45.5 square units

8. 4 cm

9. 15 cm

10. 25 : 49

11. 4 : 1

12. answers will vary; some possibilities are: 3 x 3, 5 x 1, 2 x 4

13. a. no   b. yes   c. no

14. surface area is 144π cm^2, area is 288π cm^3

15. 56.25π cm^2

16. 4 x 4 x 4

17. the better bargain is the 5.5 cm radius orange because its cost per square cm is less than the other orange

18. use the fact that 1 gal = 231 in^3; volume of water bed is 44,352 in^3 which is equivalent to 192 gallons

19. 1. b   2. d   3. f   4. e
    5. g   6. c   7. a

20. a. iv   b. iii

21. a and c produce the same result

22. A (6, 8), b (12, 4), C (2, 0)

23. answers will vary; some possibilities are: BOOK for horizontal line, MOM for vertical line

24. a and c (for b the length of sides change depending upon the size constant)

25. a. horizontal line through two opposite vertices
    b. horizontal and vertical lines, splitting rectangle in half
    c. horizontal and vertical lines, splitting figure in half

26. complete figure by reflecting segments over line of symmetry

27. a. 4   b. 2   c. 3   d. 2

28. a. 90°, 180°, 270°   b. 180°
    c. 60°, 120°   d. 180°

29. find the area of the field (5600 m^2) and take the square root; a square field with the same area should have a side length of approximately 74.83 m

30. plot points such that the ordered pairs are similar to the following: (1, 7), (2, 6), (3, 5), (4, 4), (5, 3), (6, 2), (7, 1) and then form a line to include other values

31. Area of A = 9 square units; Area of B = 15 square units

32. perimeter = $6 + 3\sqrt{2}$; area = 4.5 square units

33. if you traveled 24 hours per day, the average speed in miles per hour would be about 13.1 mph

34. The small pizza gives 3.867 inches per dollar; the medium gives 4.189 inches per dollar; the large pizza gives 3.808 inches per dollar. The medium pizza gives the most edge per dollar. The circumference of each pizza is $C = 2\pi r$.

35. a. area of square is 144 in², perimeter of square is 48 in, area of each semi-circle is 18π in², circumference of each semi-circle is 6π in

    b. area of the large circle is 36π cm², circumference of the large circle is 12π cm, the area of each small circle is 9π cm², the circumference of each small circle is 6π cm

36. sometimes a 180° rotation acts as a reflection, but only if the shape has vertical symmetry

37. yes, all quadrilaterals tessellate the plane. Each vertex point of the tessellation must be composed of each of the angles of the quadrilateral so that the sum of the angles at each vertex point is 360°.

38. a. equilateral triangle, square regular hexagon
    b. at the vertex point, there are 4 angles joined which are formed from a regular triangle, regular hexagon, regular triangle, and regular hexagon (60°, 120°, 60°, 120°)
    c. each vertex point should be surrounded by a regular triangle, a regular hexagon, another regular triangle and a regular hexagon
    d. 60° + 120° + 60° + 120° = 360° (the sum of the angles around the vertex point is 360° so there are no gaps or overlapping)

39. equilateral triangle, square, regular hexagon

40. no, the sum of the angles around the vertex point would not be 360° (435° would cause an overlap)

41. $12.50

42. 81 lbs. (3 • 3 • 3)

43. yes, the wire would be approximately 3.2 meters above the earth

44. The problem is ambiguously worded, but the intent is the find two ways to approximate the area of a circle without using a formula. There are various acceptable ways to do this among them are the following:

    Method 1: Lay the circle on grid paper (say 1 cm x 1 cm grid paper) and count the number of 1 x 1 squares it takes to cover the circle (this can be done in several ways).

    Method 2: Inscribe a square in the circle and circumscribe a square about the circle. Find the area of each circle and use the average of the two areas as the area of the circle.

45. a 2 x 5 rectangle has perimeter of 14 units and area of 10 square units, while a 6 x 6 rectangle has perimeter of 24 units and area of 36 square units

46. area = 7π (approximately 21.99 square meters)

47. 9 : 1

48. 9 : 1

49. a. no, it is quadrupled   b. it is quadrupled

50. it is the same as finding the percent of area of one square not contained in the interior of one inscribed circle: approximately 21.5%

51. a. 4 : 1   b. 2 : 1   c. 4 : 1   d. 4 : 1

52. yes, the value of the radius is squared, therefore if doubled it would actually quadruple the volume

53. divide the shape into figures that you know the areas of and then sum the individual areas

54. 52.5 square feet

55. 126 square feet

56. Not necessarily! One example is shown in the diagram below. Both polygons have 8 pins on the boundary, but the pentagon has greater perimeter than the triangle.

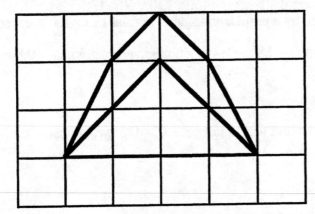

57. Finding all the non-congruent polygons with 5 boundary pins and 2 interior pins is a challenging problem. A couple of examples of these "5-2" geoboard polygons are given below (Note: Polygons A and B are not congruent, but both have 5 boundary pins and 2 interior pins). You might want to find a systematic way to list all possible polygons (so you don't duplicate any or miss any) over the next few weeks and compare your list with other students in the class. One possible way to be systematic is to look first only at triangles, then only at quadrilaterals, etc.

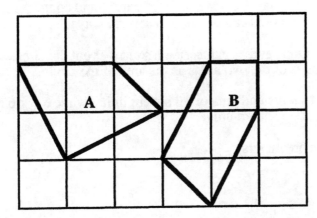

58. The polygons must have the same area, but won't necessarily have the same perimeter. A couple of examples shown below illustrate this.

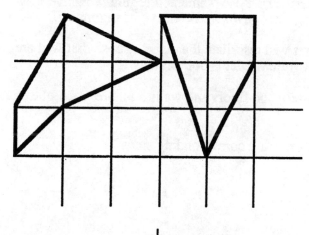

59.

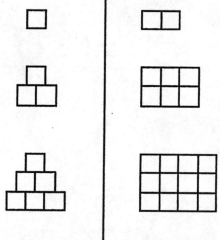

60. Cut off a right triangle on one end of the parallelogram and put it on the opposite side. It forms a rectangle because side AD is congruent to side BC and <A and <B, and <D and <C are supplementary. Thus, the area of a parallelogram is bh (the same as the area of a rectangle).

61. Rotate a copy of the trapezoid into place as shown. A parallelogram is formed since both pairs of opposite sides are parallel (bases were already parallel and angles on non-base sides are supplementary). Thus the area of a trapezoid is $1/2(b_1 + b_2)h$ (1/2 the area of a parallelogram formed by two congruent trapezoids).

62. Cut a radius in the circle and spread the circle out as shown until it forms a triangle with a base of $2\pi R$ and a height of R. Thus the area of a circle is πR^2 (the same as the area of a triangle with a base of $2\pi R$ and a height of R).

63. answers will vary

64. a. Among regular polygons, only equilateral triangles, squares, and hexagons will tessellate the plane by themselves.

    b/c. All triangles and all convex quadrilaterals will tessellate the plane. Some convex pentagons will tessellate (those for which the measures of two nonadjacent angles are 90 degrees and two pairs of sides are congruent). Also, some non regular concave pentagons will tessellate. Some non-regular convex and concave hexagons will tessellate.

    d. As noted above, some concave polygons will tessellate the plane. Those that will are such that the sum of the angles about a vertex point is 360 degrees.

    e. Answers will vary.

    f. Answers will vary. Mosaics, tiling patterns on floors and walls, etc. are good places to look for semi-regular tessellations.

65. form similar triangles and set up a proportion using corresponding sides